S0-BAE-152

**IT's ABOUT TIME®**

HERFF JONES EDUCATION DIVISION

84 Business Park Drive, Armonk, NY 10504  Phone (914) 273-2233
Fax (914) 273-2227  Toll Free (888) 698-TIME (8463)  www.its-about-time.com

**It's About Time, President**
Tom Laster

**Director of Product
Development**
Barbara Zahm, Ph.D.

**Creative/Art Director**
John Nordland

All student activities in this textbook have been designed to be as safe as possible,
and have been reviewed by professionals specifically for that purpose. As well, appropriate warnings
concerning potential safety hazards are included where applicable to particular activities.
However, responsibility for safety remains with the student, the classroom
teacher, the school principals, and the school board.

It's About Time® is a registered trademark of It's About Time, Herff Jones Education Division.

ArcView® and ESRI® are Registered Trademarks of ESRI.

Registered names and trademarks, etc., used in this publication, even without specific indication thereof,
are not to be considered unprotected by law.

Copyright ©2005 by Northwestern University. All rights reserved.

All rights reserved. No part of this publication may be reproduced, stored in a retrieval system,
or transmitted, in any form or by any means, electronic, mechanical, photocopying,
recording, or otherwise, without the prior written permission of the copyright owner.

Care has been taken to trace the ownership of copyright material contained
in this publication. The publisher will gladly receive any information that will
rectify any reference or credit line in subsequent editions.

Printed and bound in the United States of America.

ISBN-10: 1-58591-446-0

ISBN-13: 978-1-58591-446-3

1 2 3 4 5 VH 09 08 07 06 05

This material is based upon work supported by the National Science Foundation under
grants No. RED-9453715, ESI-9720687, DGE-9714534. Any opinions, findings, and conclusions or
recommendations expressed in this material are those of the author(s) and do not necessarily reflect
the views of the National Science Foundation.

# INVESTIGATIONS IN
# ENVIRONMENTAL
# SCIENCE

**Unit 3: Water Management**

## A CASE-BASED APPROACH
## TO THE STUDY OF
## ENVIRONMENTAL SYSTEMS

Daniel C. Edelson Ph.D.

Developed by

**The Geographic Data in Education (GEODE) Initiative**

**Northwestern University**

GEODE INITIATIVE — Geographic Data in Education

In association with

IT's **ABOUT** TIME ®

HERFF JONES EDUCATION DIVISION

**Project Director**
Daniel C. Edelson Ph.D.

**Lead Curriculum Developers**
Kathleen Schwille
Meridith Bruozas
Michael Lach
Michael Taber
Douglas Gordin

**Curriculum Developers**
Kylene Chinsio
Natalie Goldstein
Adam Tarnoff

**Lead Developer,**
**Teacher Edition**
Ann Rivet

**Developer,**
**Teacher Edition**
Amy Emmert

**Consultants**
Duane Griffin
Brad Sageman

**Contributors**
Janet Bell-Wehr
Jennifer Coyle
Matthew Cruz
Douglas Goodwin
Lisa Kenyon
Shanna McGarry
Petra Pancoskova
Cynthia Quinn
Colleen Riley
Marc Siciliano
Darlene Slusher
Craig Smith
Jean Sutow
Susan Trzaskus

**Pilot And**
**Field Test Teachers**
Janet Bell-Wehr
Lori Blackburn
Anne Bogardt
Staci Bynum
Patricia Carlson
Mollie David
Julie Dowling
Theresa Dzoga-Borg
Jayne Entihar
Roger Felch
Linda Fleming
Douglas Goodwin
Nina Hike-Teague
Lloyd Kiefer
Gloria Latta
Cynthia Lauster
Chris Nichols
Phyllis Nicholson
Lars Nelson
Danielle Oplaski
John Pritchard
Gwynna Reinhardt
Delvena Riggins-Dawes
Antoinette Rubalcaba
Cliff Schlund
Tamara Shibayama
Marc Siciliano
Julia Somers
Dawn Teaschner
Peter Thomas
Susan Trzaskus
Ray Tschillard
Eric Wheeler
Steve Wilson

**Programmers**
Brian Clark
Peter Moore
Eric Russell
Christopher Kadel
Ben Loh
Laura Ferguson
Hisham Petry

**Geospatial Data Development**
Terry Hammarquist
Michael Smith

**Undergraduate**
**Research Assistants**
Eddy Ameen
Tajuana Bates
Eric Hanson
Aaron Hosmon
Benjamin Johnson
Steve Juh
Danielle Lessovitz
Ray Liu
Michael Nam
Viktoria Wang

**Evaluation**
*SRI International*
Principal Investigators:
  Roy Pea
  William Penuel
Dan Zalles
Valerie Crawford
Yukie Toyama

*The Learning Partnership*
Principal Investigator:
Steven McGee

**WorldWatcher**
**Curriculum Project**
Daniel C. Edelson,
Principal Investigator
Louis M. Gomez,
Co-Principal Investigator

## Advisory Board

James Hays, Ph.D.
Lamont-Doherty Earth Observatory
Columbia University

James Hansen, Ph.D.
NASA Goddard Institute for Space
Science

George Tselioudis, Ph.D.
NASA Goddard Institute for Space
Science

Mary Marlino, Ph.D.
Digital Library for Earth Systems
Education,
University Corporation for
Atmospheric Research
Boulder, CO

Kathryn Keranen
Great Falls, VA

Mary Ellen Verona, Ph.D.
Maryland Virtual High School
Silver Spring, MD

Mark Horrell, Ph.D.
Illinois Math and Science Academy

Prassede Calabi, Ph.D.
Black Cat Consulting
Winchester, MA

Herbert Their
Lawrence Hall of Science
University of California, Berkeley

Joe McInerney, Ph.D.
National Coalition for Health
Professional Education in Genetics

Michael Goodchild, Ph.D.
National Center for Geographic
Information and Analysis
University of California, Santa
Barbara

## Safety Reviewer
Carl Heltzel, Ph.D.
Transylvania University

## External Reviewers
Derek Aday, Ph.D.
Department of Evolution, Ecology,
and Organismal Biology
Ohio State University

Heidi Anderson
Yellowstone Center for Resources

Comfort Ateh, Ph.D.
University of California, Davis

Denis Bacon, Ed.D.
College of Agricultural Sciences
and Technology
California State University, Fresno

Dave Bayless, Ph.D., P.E.
State of Ohio Coal Research Center
Ohio University

Jason Box, Ph.D.
Department of Geography
Ohio State University

Carrie Schaefer Bucki

Michael Cain
Department of Applied Biology
Rose-Hulman Institute of
Technology

Will Cantrell, Ph.D.
Physics Department
Michigan Technological University

Susan Cassels
Office of Population Research
Princeton Univeristy

Michael Chang, Ph.D.
School of Earth & Atmospheric
Sciences
Georgia Institute of Technology

Ian Clark
School of Natural & Built
Environment
University of South Australia

Barbara Cooper, Ph.D.
Purdue University

John Costa
U.S. Geological Survey

David Flaspohler, Ph.D.
School of Forest Resources &
Environmental Science
Michigan Technological University

Rong Fu, Ph.D.
School of Earth & Atmospheric
Sciences
Georgia Institute of Technology

Brett Hamlin, Ph.D.
School of Engineering
Michigan Technological University

Jerry Hatfield
USDA/ARS National Soil Tilth
Laboratory

L. Gregory Huey, Ph.D.
School of Earth & Atmospheric
Sciences
Georgia Institute of Technology

Craig Kallsen
Farm Advisor
University of California,
Cooperative Extension

Mary Kleb
NASA Langley Research Center

Brian Kloeppel, Ph.D.
COWEETA Hydrologic Laboratory
University of Georgia

John LaBoon
U.S. Bureau of Reclamation

Nathanael T. Lauster, Ph,D.
University of British Columbia

Kevin Lien
Portland Community College

Joseph Moran, Ph.D.
American Meteorological Society
University of Wisconsin, Green Bay

John Mull, Ph,D.
Department of Zoology
Weber State University

Larry Nuss
U.S. Bureau of Reclamation

Rebecca Redhorse, M.S.

William Reinert, Ph.D.

Ron Reuter, Ph.D.
Department of Forest Resources
Oregon State University, Cascades
Campus

Jennifer Rhode, Ph.D.
Department of Biology and
Environmental Science
Georgia College and State
University

George Rudins
U.S. Department of Energy

Del Smith, P.E.
U.S. Bureau of Reclamation

Michelle Sneed
California Water Science Center
U.S. Geological Survey

John Richard Stepp, Ph.D.
University of Florida

Lynn Wright
Oak Ridge National Laboratory

Don Wuebbles, Ph.D.
Department of Atmospheric
Sciences
University of Illinois

# Unit Three Credits

**Chapter 1: Soil**
LESSON 2F (PAGE 26): Soil texture triangle courtesy The Institute of Food and
Agricultural Sciences (IFAS), University of Florida
LESSONS 3B (PAGE 32): Peat moss photograph courtesy of The Provincial Museum of Alberta, Botany
Program;

**Chapter 2: Agriculture**
LESSON 3A (PAGE 85): Corn growth illustration courtesy Robert Wilson, University of Nebraska;
LESSON 3B (PAGE 87): Fresno evapotranspiration data courtesy California Irrigation Management
Information System, California Department of Water Resources;
LESSONS 5C (PAGE 104): Fresno precipitation data courtesy California Irrigation Management Information
System, California Department of Water Resources;
LESSONS 6D (PAGE 120): Fresno evapotranspiration and precipitation data courtesy California Irrigation
Management Information System, California Department of Water Resources;

**Chapter 3: Dams**
LESSON 1B (PAGE 131): Photograph of Maguga Dam (embankment) courtesy of Komati Basin Water
Authority, Swaziland; (PAGE 132): Photograph of Grand Coulee Dam (gravity) courtesy U.S. Department of
Interior, Bureau of Reclamation; Photograph of Theodore Roosevelt Dam (arch) courtesy U.S. Department of
Interior, Bureau of Reclamation; (PAGE 132): Photograph of Bartlett Dam (buttress) courtesy of the U.S.
Department of Interior, Bureau of Reclamation;
LESSON 2B (PAGE 139): Arcview screenshots courtesy Environmental Systems Research Institute, Inc.
(ESRI) Redlands, CA 92373-8100 www.esri.com
LESSONS 3B, 3C, 3D (PAGES 149, 151, 153): Topographic maps courtesy United States Geological Survey;
LESSON 4A (PAGE 156): Hydrograph courtesy NWIS Database, U.S. Geological Survey, accessed July 2004;
LESSON 4C (PAGE 163): Rio Grande discharge data courtesy U.S. Geological Survey

**Chapter 4: Salmon**
LESSON 1C (PAGE 190): Sacramento River Watershed map courtesy Regional Monitoring Program for Trace
Substances in the San Francisco Estuary (administered by the San Francisco Estuary Institute); Spawning
salmon data courtesy California Department of Fish and Game;
LESSON 2A (PAGE 194): Sea lion photograph courtesy the National Oceanic and Atmospheric Administration
(NOAA) - National Marine Fisheries Service
LESSONS 2B (PAGE 197): Fish ladder photograph courtesy Jim Steinborn;

**Chapter 5: Aquifers**
LESSON 3C (PAGE 234): Saltwater intrusion diagram from Cooper, H.H., Jr., 1964, A hypothesis concerning
the dynamic balance of fresh water and salt water in a coastal aquifer: U.S. Geological Survey Water-Supply
Paper 1613-C, p. 1-12; (PAGE 235): Photograph of sinkhole courtesy Deborah Buffington;
LESSON 4A (PAGE 238): Map of California aquifers courtesy of the U.S. Geological Survey;
LESSONS 4B (PAGE 240): Watershed diagram from Watershed Professionals Network 1999 Oregon
Watershed Assessment Manual, June 1999, prepared for the Governor's Watershed Enhancement Board,
Salem, Oregon;
LESSON 4C (PAGE 243): Map of California watersheds courtesy of the California Spatial Information Library;
LESSONS 7A (PAGE 263): Inputs and Outputs to Fresno aquifers data courtesy Fresno Water Management.

# Table of Contents

# Soil

# Chapter 1
# Soil

## Connections

This chapter begins your study of water resources and how they are managed. The title of the chapter might seem confusing at first. What does soil have to do with water? Soil has a lot to do with water and one connection between them is agriculture, or farming. As the human population grows, there is a greater demand for food and for a wider variety of foods. In developed countries, consumers are no longer satisfied with a choice of just a few types of vegetables. We demand a tremendous variety of high-quality produce, since most people no longer have the option of growing their own. Thousands of different types of fruits and vegetables are imported into the U.S. each year from around the world to satisfy consumers' desire for new and exotic flavors. This variety comes in part from the soil and water that makes plants grow. In other parts of the world, the soil and water conditions can be very different from those found in the U.S.

You will begin this chapter by learning about one region of the country where much of our food is grown—the great Central Valley of California. This important agricultural region provides 98% of the nation's broccoli. It is also the second-largest grower of tomatoes in the U.S., with a record yield of 12 million tons of tomatoes in 1999. It is a major producer of melons, avocados, artichokes, grapes, and many other vegetables and fruits consumed here and exported abroad. This high level of production comes at a price, however. You will learn about the conflict that is raging in California over farmers' use of water and the water shortages this causes for others. This shortage is the focus of this unit. How can the water budget for this region of California be balanced to satisfy the needs of all the people who rely on the water supply to live? Is there room in that water budget for the natural environment? Or have our past actions in the region ruined all hope for thriving natural ecosystems? Some of the answers to these questions can be found under your feet—in the soil.

## In this chapter:

After hearing from several groups that are involved in the conflict over California's water, you will learn more about soil. You will classify soils and you will design an experiment to determine what type of soil is best for growing plants. An important part of your soil analysis will be determining soil's ability to hold water.

## When you're done you'll be able to:

- predict the type of soil that is best for growing crops.

- use a soil texture triangle to categorize soils based on the amount of silt, clay and sand in them.

- calculate the amount of water a fertile soil capable of sustaining crops can hold.

# Lesson 1
# Water Issues

 ***Driving Question:*** *Why is there controversy in Fresno about water?*

## Overview

In this lesson, you will be introduced to the community of Fresno, California. Members of this community disagree about how their water should be used and who should be able to use it. Because of the growing population in the area, residents are demanding more water resources. However, the region's farmers do not want to lose their share of the water to homes and businesses.

In the first activity, you will become familiar with different viewpoints on the water shortage. You will explore each group's claims in more detail. You will identify who was stating only their opinion and who was arguing based on evidence. Finally, you will devise a plan for conducting more research on this problem to help develop a solution.

## Important Content

- Many different issues are involved in deciding how to address a region's water problems.

- Farmers, environmentalists, and ordinary citizens all have a stake in the outcome.

# The Harry Winter Show

**Essential Question:** *Why do people disagree about how to distribute water in Fresno County?*

## Overview

In this activity, you will be introduced to some of the issues facing Fresno County in central California. It is a mixed urban and rural area with an arid climate. It is located near the San Joaquin River, but needs to meet the diverse water needs of all of its residents. Read the attached script and answer the analysis question.

## Procedure

Read the script "The Harry Winter Show" and act it out in class according to your teacher's instructions.

## Analysis Question

1. Answer the essential question: *Why do people disagree about how to distribute water in Fresno County?*

# The Harry Winter Show

<u>Cast of Characters</u>
(in order of appearance)

| | |
|---|---|
| Harry Winter | Host |
| Sarah Million | Environmental Rules Organization |
| Michael Turney | Resident of Fresno, CA |
| Laura Lopez | Fresno County farmer |
| Audience Member 1 | Resident of Lake Powell, UT |
| Audience | |

Setting: *Talk-show style TV set*

**Harry Winter:** Today's guests are here from Fresno, California to talk about some of their water issues. We have Sarah Million, from the Environment Rules Organization. She is here to say that water issues in California need to be addressed before precious fish die, water quality diminishes, and rivers and lakes turn into muddy sludge. Michael Turney, a resident of Fresno, agrees that there is a major water shortage but doesn't feel responsible for it. He thinks farmers in the Valley are guilty of all the water guzzling. Laura Lopez, a Fresno farmer, is here because she's tired of getting blamed for consuming all the water. She's here to say that it's not her fault that the water in Fresno will soon be gone. Sarah, let's start with you. Why is the water in Fresno something we need to focus on?

**Million:** Well, Harry, water in Fresno is scarce. Let's just say that if the environment were a human, I would send it to a doctor before it gets any worse. In many ways, water is the blood of the Earth. If water is tainted or scarce, everything—from fish to wetlands, from insects to humans—will suffer. As concerned citizens of the planet, we need to take care of the Earth before it can no longer support us.

**Harry Winter:** Well, don't you think this can wait?

**Million:** No, we've waited long enough! Pretty soon, both residents and farmers will have to find new aquifers to pull water from. They may have to get water from places much farther away, and it won't come cheap. The era of being able to go farther west to exploit new resources is over. It is now time for us to take a long, hard look at what we have, what we've done, and what sort of state we want California to be.

**Lopez:** I just want to say that everyone has this idea that getting more water for California is so complex. It's really quite easy. During the wet season, our farmland tends to flood and during the dry season, we just don't have enough water. What we need to do is create more storage water for farmers. We need more dams.

**Million:** Right now, the state of California has over 1,400 dams. One more dam is not the solution.

**Lopez:** You don't need to be Einstein to figure this out. If you're against building another dam, we could increase the height of a pre-existing dam. That way, during the wet season, I don't have to watch water being wasted. I can just put it in storage. And during the dry season, I can just take the water out and use it to irrigate my fields. It would be like a water bank.

**Million:** Dams are terrible for the environment. Even increasing the height of an existing dam, like Shasta or Friants, would have serious environmental repercussions. By holding water that would naturally flow down the river, the rivers become little trickles barely able to sustain fish. Some of these fish are on the verge of extinction. Dams and diversions have also blocked steelhead and salmon access to over 90% of their original habitat.

**Lopez:** We could use some of the extra water stored in the larger dam to help restore the downstream habitats for the fish.

**Million:** To make a dam larger would not help the fish. You may increase the downstream flow during rainy times, but during the dry season, when reservoirs are low, irrigating crops will be more of a priority. The fish will suffer. We need a solution that will be viable in the long run.

**Lopez:** The dams are the best option for right now. They've worked so far.

**Million:** Yeah, they've worked to kill fish and destroy water quality. Dams are very inefficient at storing water. Evaporation causes much of the water to disappear. And don't forget agricultural runoff often finds its way into the reservoirs. This causes the water to become saltier and filled with toxic heavy metals that destroy water quality.

**Turney:** I've stayed quiet this whole time. Now it's time for me to say that I will not support the construction of a new dam, or even making any of the current dams any larger. Who do you think pays for these big water projects? Taxpaying citizens have to bear the cost of these expensive projects. We citizens foot the bill through our taxes, and then we watch as others get the payoff. I refuse to pay more money for something that's too expensive and doesn't work.

**Harry Winter:** Let's ask an audience member for an opinion

**Audience Member 1:** I agree with the environmental lady. I live down by Lake Powell in Utah, a lake that was created by flooding the Glen Canyon after they built Glen Canyon Dam. That dam and the reservoir it created ruined sacred Native American land. It has become the destination for loud boaters throwing parties and polluting the already filthy water. I also know that each year, the dam holds less and less water because of silt build-up.

**Harry Winter:** Did you hear that folks? He said that dams become less efficient over the years.

**Turney:** Farmers need to sacrifice some of the water they're getting now for the good of the community!!

**Audience:** Oh!

**Lopez:** How dare you say that! We need the little water that we get now. The food that we produce is for the good of the community. You need to remember that food doesn't grow in the grocery store, food grows on farms. Without us farmers, and without water for us, there is no food.

**Turney:** Giving less water to the farmers in California is no big deal. There are other places in the United States where people can farm.

**Lopez:** No big deal? That's where you're wrong again! California farmers produce nearly half of all the fruits, vegetables, and nuts consumed by the people of the United States. And remember, 20% of our products go overseas! You should think twice before claiming that "less water for farmers is not a big deal." Crops depend on water. People depend on us for food. It's that simple.

**Million:** Nowadays, there are ways farmers can use water more efficiently. Drip irrigation and micro-irrigation are two methods that come to mind. They allow farmers to give plants the exact amount of water they need without losing as much to seepage and evaporation.

**Lopez:** We've been looking into those options, but they're just too expensive. If we want keep prices low for the consumer, we have to take the cheapest route possible. Right now, it costs about $2000 to perfectly level one hectare of farmland using lasers. Leveling the land helps because I wouldn't need as much water for irrigation. The water would get evenly spread out over the land. But the initial cost is just so high and with water prices the way they are, I would be throwing my money away. The only farmers who can use those techniques are the rich ones who have the resources. I'm not wealthy; I'm just trying to make a living.

**Turney:** Yeah, trying to make a living by sucking all the water out of the Earth while government subsidies make your water so cheap, you can water alfalfa with it.

**Audience:** Oh!

**Lopez:** What's wrong with alfalfa?

**Turney:** Alfalfa needs more water than a sponge the size of India. It's a thirsty plant and shouldn't be grown in an area where water isn't easy to come by.

**Lopez:** Why is it that everyone is blaming farmers? You're not so innocent yourself.

**Turney:** Me? I don't know what you're talking about.

**Audience:** Boo!

**Harry Winter:** Is there something you should tell us Michael?

**Turney:** I don't know what Laura is talking about.

**Lopez:** I'm a fourth-generation farmer. If there's anything I know a great deal about, it's water and the way people use it!!

**Audience:** Tell Us! Tell Us!

**Lopez:** Right now, the people of Fresno pay a flat fee for their water. This means that homeowners can wash their cars and water their lawns as much as they want. So while farmers are thinking of ways to squeeze value out of each drop of water, citizens are pouring it down the drain and doing it under everyone's noses!

**Turney:** That's not true! Hey, did we complain when the government spent millions of taxpayer dollars on building dams and subsidizing water for agriculture? No! The least you could do is have a little respect for the way we choose to pay for our water. And even if we do use water a bit loosely, it won't make that much of a difference, because agriculture uses over 80% of all the water. So even if Fresno residents did reduce the amount of water they use, it wouldn't solve our water shortage problem.

**Lopez:** You have to widen your perspective and try to look into the future. With urban sprawl eating up the landscape, more and more residents will use more and more water. Fresno's area population is projected to grow 79% by 2020. Starting conservation methods now will increase the immediate supply of water. If the thousands of new Fresno residents do the same, a ripple effect will occur and have a great impact. I say we make the citizens of Fresno put meters on their water and make people pay for the water they actually use!

**Turney:** Back in 1992, we debated whether or not to make residents install water meters. The voters clearly said "no!" We don't want to pay with meters because we fear the government will have an easier time increasing our water bills. Also, the up-front costs of installing a meter in every house would be huge. In 1992, we agreed to pay more for our water at a price that's competitive with water meter prices. Also, we decided to make it mandatory for new houses to be built with water meters. So the residents are already doing their part to conserve water.

**Million:** I think water meters are a good idea. Most of the nation uses water meters anyway. Los Angeles, which has metered water, has had the same rates of water consumption since 1984 even with population explosions.

**Audience:** METERS! METERS! METERS!

**Turney:** We already pay a lot for our water!

**Lopez:** It's the only way to force people to save water!

**Million:** There are lots of little things residents can do to save water and people would do them if it saved them money. Little things like taking shorter showers, watering lawns at night instead of during the day, and reusing old water for plants just to name a few.

**Lopez:** Yeah, if water is metered, residents might even look into buying toilets that use less water or showerheads that do the same. There's even water heaters that attach to their kitchen sink so they wouldn't have to let the water run too long before it gets warm.

**Million:** But what are you going to do about the farmers already using more water than we can afford?

**Turney:** I think we should encourage farmers to use conservation techniques like drip irrigation, which allows them to produce the same number of crops with much less water. That way, we could take some land out of production and use it to build homes on later on.

**Lopez:** If you're such an environmentalist, why can't you see that farms are a part of the environment and actually help the environment?

**Turney:** How do farms help the rivers and fish that are being destroyed this moment?

**Audience:** You kill fish! You kill fish!

**Turney:** If I could make a salmon speak, I'd bring it here and have it tell you its story. I would bring it here to stand before you and say, "I'm a one hundred and seventy-thousandth generation Californian and I'm here to ask where did my backyard go? What happened to the free-flowing waters? What happened to the marshes that used to take the floodwaters? You've built dams, you dirtied my rivers, you choked my eggs, and you made my friends extinct." Since I can't do that, all I can do is argue on behalf of the salmon and say that it's time we right all the wrongs that we've done.

**Harry Winter:** I want to thank all of the guests for being with us today. It's time for a final thought. We all have our issues. It's important that these issues get resolved before time, or water, runs out. It's up to the members of this audience to think about the future, to think about how their water should be used, and to think about what choices they will make when they become voters. I urge you to take a good look at water in the west and think of ways to solve the problem.

# Evidence and Opinion

***Essential Question:*** *What missing pieces of evidence are needed to support the statements of the stakeholders?*

## Overview

When making an argument, people often present a combination of evidence and opinion to support their claim. You know the difference between evidence and opinion, but how often do you think about it when listening to someone make an argument? In this activity, you will examine the arguments made by stakeholders in "The Harry Winter Show" and distinguish between evidence and opinion. You will then present your findings to the rest of the class.

## Procedure

1. As a class, you will make two stakeholder charts based on "The Harry Winter Show" script from the last activity. Your teacher will assign you to one character in the script. Complete Step 2 for your character, and share your answers with the class.

2. For your character, record the following information for each stakeholder chart.
   - Character name and **stakeholder group** they represent.
   - **Effects** on that group of reducing the water farmers can use (Chart 1), or effects on the stakeholder if farmers can use the same amount or more water (Chart 2).
   - Indicate whether the effect is supported by **evidence** or **opinions**.

3. As a class, combine your rows into two completed charts.

## Analysis Questions

1. Did any of the people interviewed in "The Harry Winter Show" support their arguments with evidence? If so, which ones?

2. For those people who did not use evidence, how did they try to convince you that they are correct? Were they convincing?

3. Answer the essential question: *What missing pieces of evidence are needed to support the statements of the stakeholders?*

## Stakeholders' chart if farmers are required to use less water

| Who are the **stakeholders** that will be affected by this action? (include **character** name) | In what way(s) will they be affected? (Note whether there is **evidence** to support the statement, or if it is an **opinion**) | + or – | Is this effect the intended goal of the action or is it a side effect? | Has the stakeholder placed himself/herself in this position voluntarily and with appropriate understanding of the risks involved? |
|---|---|---|---|---|
| | | | | |
| | | | | |
| | | | | |
| | | | | |
| | | | | |
| | | | | |
| | | | | |
| | | | | |
| | | | | |

**Stakeholders' chart if farmers are allowed to maintain and/or increase their water use**

| Who are the **stakeholders** that will be affected by this action? (include **character** name) | In what way(s) will they be affected? (Note whether there is **evidence** to support the statement, or if it is an **opinion**) | + or – | Is this effect the intended goal of the action or is it a side effect? | Has the stakeholder placed himself/herself in this position voluntarily and with appropriate understanding of the risks involved? |
|---|---|---|---|---|
| | | | | |
| | | | | |
| | | | | |
| | | | | |
| | | | | |
| | | | | |
| | | | | |
| | | | | |

# Fresno Situation

 **Essential Question:** *What is the disagreement over water in Fresno all about?*

## Overview

In the last few activities, you have read about disagreements in Fresno, California about how to manage their water supply. There are many stakeholders involved in this situation. They all have different needs and ideas for what should be done with the water in the community. Because fresh water is a limited resource, the same kinds of issues that are coming up in California are coming up all over the United States and the world. To help you understand these issues, you will explore the challenges of water resources in Fresno and search for a solution throughout this unit. In this activity, you will begin to pose questions about the situation in Fresno. You will also consider what you will need to learn before you can decide on a solution.

## Discussion Questions

After reading "The Harry Winter Show," what questions do you have about Fresno and the stakeholders there?

What questions do you have about the water situation and the science behind where water comes from and how it gets to the people who use it?

In Lesson 1: *Evidence and Opinion*, you made a list of the types of evidence missing from some people's arguments. How might you find that evidence?

Is your community having disagreements over how water is used? Have you ever had a drought or water restrictions in your area? Was your situation similar to what you know about Fresno? Why or why not?

## Lesson 2
# Mechanical Analysis of Soil

***Driving Question:*** *How are soils different?*

## Overview

The previous lesson described the challenges of managing water supplies in California's Central Valley. Much of the water is used for agriculture, which has caused tension between farmers and citizens of Fresno. In this lesson, you will start to look at agriculture and how water is used to grow crops. Soil is a critical ingredient for agriculture, so we will start by learning about soil. You will learn about the different particles that soil is made of, and you will explore the properties of the particles. By analyzing and classifying soil in this way, you can learn about different soils in your own area and in California. In the next several lessons, you will learn about how soil holds water. This will help you to understand the relationship between the type of soil in a location and the amount of water that must be supplied to grow plants.

## Important Content

- There are three components of soil: mineral matter, organic matter, and pore space. The mineral component is a mixture of particles of stones, gravel, sand, silt, and clay.

- These different soil particles have different sizes and the way the particles hold together gives a soil structure.

- A soil's texture is determined by the amount of sand, silt and clay in the soil.

# Many Kinds Of Plants

 **Essential Question:** *What are the connections between soil type and the plants that grow in the soil?*

## Overview

Your teacher has placed samples of several different kinds of plants around the classroom. In this activity, you will make some observations about these plants to determine what they all have in common.

## Safety

Follow standard safety rules and school safety rules for laboratory activities.

## Procedure

1. Work with a group. As a group, make three observations about each of the plants and the soil they grow in. Create a data table to record your observations.

2. As a group, decide on five things all the plants have in common. Make a list of those things and be prepared to share your list with the class.

## Discussion Questions

1. What did you initially observe about the plants?

2. What, if anything, did you observe that showed a relationship between the plants and the type of soil they were growing in?

3. Why do you think soil is so important to plant growth?

4. Answer the essential question: *What are the connections between soil type and the plants that grow in the soil?*

# Hands On Soil

**Essential Question:** *How do soil structures differ?*

## Overview

Soil type is a major variable that affects plant growth. In this activity, you will examine some different soils. Soils are made of three components: minerals of different sizes, organic materials from the remains of dead plants and animals, and pore space that can be filled with water and air.

Soil structure is the way soil particles are held together in what are called peds. Peds come in a variety of shapes, depending on the texture, composition, and environment.

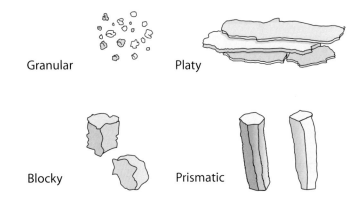

Granular   Platy

Blocky   Prismatic

## Materials

soil samples
water
plastic spoon
centimeter ruler
white paper
magnifying glass

## Safety

Follow standard safety rules and school safety rules for laboratory activities.

## Procedure

1. Create a data table with the following headers: Color, Ped Size, Ped Shape, Average Ped Mass, Dustiness, and Other.

2. Look at the white paper to determine dustiness. Soils that are dusty will leave fine particles on the paper. Soils that are less dusty will not. Rank the soils in order of most dusty ("1") to least dusty ("5").

3. Mix each soil sample with a small amount of water until the soil is just damp.

4. Record the color of each sample.

5. Use the ruler to measure the diameter of a medium-sized ped in each sample. Record your results in the Ped Size column.

6. Use the illustrations above to identify the ped shape that is most common in your soil sample. You may need to use the magnifying glass to observe details in the sample.

7. To calculate the average ped mass, place a small number of peds on the electronic balance and record the mass. Divide by the number of peds and record your result.

8. Record anything unusual or notable about your soil in the Other column.

## Analysis Questions

1. Which soil type do you think has the most spaces between particles?

2. Which soil type do you think would hold water best? Explain your reasoning.

3. Answer the essential question: *How do soil structures differ?*

# Composition of Soil

**Essential Question:** *What are the three components of soil?*

## Overview

Read the following article and answer the analysis questions below.

## Composition of Soil

Soil is everywhere; it is probably on the bottom of your shoe right now. It covers almost every inch of the Earth. Much of our life is influenced by the behavior of the soil around our houses, roads, septic and sewage disposal systems, airports, parks, recreation sites, farms, forests, schools, and shopping centers. What is constructed on land should be guided by the soil composition. Like snowflakes, no two soils are exactly alike.

### Composition of a Typical Soil Sample

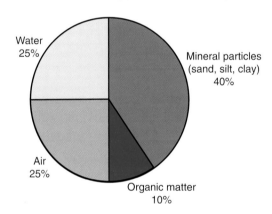

Water 25%

Mineral particles (sand, silt, clay) 40%

Air 25%

Organic matter 10%

### *Definition of Soil*

Soil is the substance that vegetation grows in. Soil is a mixture of mineral material, organic material, and pore spaces. The mineral material can be sand, silt, clay or a combination of these. Some soils are sandy. Sand is composed of large-sized minerals, primarily silica ($SiO2$). Some soils are silty. Silt is composed of mid-sized minerals, primarily powdered rock with mixed chemical composition. Some soils are clay. Clay is made of small-sized particles. There are a number of different types of clays. Most are compounds containing aluminum, silicon, and oxygen, along with calcium, magnesium, and potassium. Soils can contain varying amounts of organic material, which comes primarily from plants. Finally, soil consists of pore spaces, which are the pockets of air and water between the solid materials that make up the soil. The particular combination of mineral and organic materials and the pore spaces are the characteristics that determine how well the soil will support plant life.

It takes tens of thousands of years for a typical topsoil to reach full maturity. Minerals become part of soil as the original material (rock) erodes or weathers due to climate, time, topography, and organism (plants and animals) decay. Soil is a "superficial" medium in which plants and other organisms grow. Soil nourishes plant life with nutrients and water. Soil is the foundation for life.

## Size of Soil Particles

Stones and cobbles: larger than 64 mm
Gravel: 2 mm to 76 mm
Sand: 0.05 to 2 mm
Silt: 0.002 to 0.05 mm
Clay: less than 0.002 mm

## Soil Layers

Soils develop into layers over time. Most soils are stratified into horizontal layers called soil horizons, which reveal a great deal about the history and usefulness of the soil. The thickness, color, texture, and composition of each horizon are used to classify the soil. The A Horizon is called topsoil and includes a varying percentage of organic matter. The B Horizon is called subsoil and often includes clay as well as leached chemicals such as iron. The C Horizon is the material from which the soil is derived. Some soils can overlay bedrock called an R horizon. Different soils may vary in their color, texture, structure, aeration, and drainage.

# Analysis Questions

1. What are three mineral components of soil?

2. What are three soil horizons? What is the major characteristic of each?

3. Answer the essential question: *What are the three components of soil?*

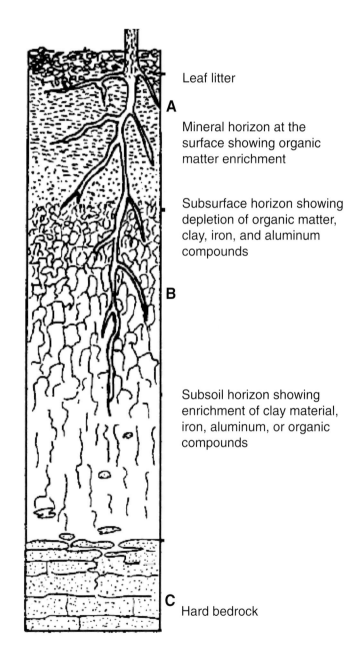

Leaf litter

**A**

Mineral horizon at the surface showing organic matter enrichment

Subsurface horizon showing depletion of organic matter, clay, iron, and aluminum compounds

**B**

Subsoil horizon showing enrichment of clay material, iron, aluminum, or organic compounds

**C** Hard bedrock

Soil

# Soil Sieves

**Essential Question:** *Estimate the percentages of sand versus silt/clay in the soil samples.*

## Overview

In this activity, you will use a sieve to investigate the size of different soil particles. You will use the following definitions:

stones and cobbles: bigger than 76 mm in diameter.

gravel: 2 mm to 76 mm in diameter.

sand: 0.05 to 2 mm in diameter.

silt: 0.002 to .05 mm in diameter.

clay: less than 0.002 mm in diameter

## Materials

soil sieve: 2 mm aperture
soil sieve: 0.05 mm aperture
5 soil samples

## Safety

Follow standard safety rules and school safety rules for laboratory activities.

## Procedure

1. Sift one soil sample through the largest sieve to separate it into two piles. In your notebook, describe the properties of the soil in each pile.

2. Select the pile that has smaller size particles. Use the smaller sieve to separate this pile into two piles. (You should now have three piles.) Describe the properties of the new piles of soil with smaller particles.

3. Repeat the process for the other four soil samples. In your notebook, describe the similarities and differences you observe in the five soil samples.

## Analysis Questions

1. Make a sketch of a typical particle from each soil sample. Draw the soil particle sizes relative to the others.

2. What is the biggest sized particle that could be in the second pile? How do you know?

3. Which pile has the most sand? Which has the most silt and clay? Which has the most gravel?

4. Answer the essential question: *Estimate the percentages of sand versus silt/clay in the soil samples.*

# Settling

**Essential Questions:** *Did this method of measurement give different or the same results as the sieves? Why do you think this happened?*

## Overview

In this activity, you will investigate how to break down soil into separate particle sizes using a settling method. Each soil sample will be mixed with water and Calgon, a chemical that helps separate particles in the soil.

## Materials

soil sieve
200-mL beaker
1 one-quart jar
8% Calgon solution
tap water
one soil sample
ruler

## Safety

Follow standard safety rules and school safety rules for laboratory activities.

## Procedure

1. Remove sticks, leaves and gravel from your soil sample.

2. Fill the 200-mL beaker with soil. (Don't pack down the soil.) Empty the soil into the one-quart jar. The soil should be between 50 mm and 70 mm high.

3. Add 100 mL of the 8% Calgon solution and fill the jar nearly to the top with water (leave about 30 mm of room at the top). Cap the jar tightly and shake it vigorously for 10 minutes. Place the jar on a desk or table where it will not be disturbed. It should look like the jar in Figure 1.

**Figure 1:** Soil, water, and Calgon immediately after shaking.

4. Let the jar stand for 20 minutes. Do not shake or move it again from its storage spot because it will cause errors. Clean up your work area.

5. Measure the total depth of settled soil in millimeters. Record this number on your data table.

### Stop and Think

After adding water and shaking, why is the total depth greater than it was after Step 2?

6. After 20 minutes, measure the depth of the bottom layer of sand in millimeters and record on the data table.

7. Measure the depth of the middle layer of silt.

8. The layer on the top is the clay portion of the sample. It is a thin layer of very fine particles. Measure the clay layer.

9. Let the jar sit overnight. The next day, repeat the measurements in Steps 6 through 8.

**Figure 2:** Clay soil and Calgon after settling.

**Figure 3:** Clay-Loam, soil and Calgon after settling.

## Analysis Questions

1. Convert both your 20-minute and final measurements into percentages of each layer per total amount of soil. Be sure to show your work.

2. Why do you think the measurements were different for the 20-minute and 24-hour readings? What does this tell you about the possible error in this experiment?

3. Answer the essential questions: *Did this method of measurement give different or the same results as the sieves? Why do you think this happened?*

### *Soil 2: Settling Data Table*

| Layer | After 20 Minutes | | After 24 Hours | |
|---|---|---|---|---|
| | mm | % | mm | % |
| Sand | | | | |
| Silt | | | | |
| Clay | | | | |
| Total Depth | | 100% | | 100% |

# The Texture Triangle

**Essential Question:** *Explain how the soil texture triangle describes the texture of soils.*

## Overview

You have learned that soil is a mixture of mineral material, organic matter, and pore space. In a typical sample of topsoil, minerals account for 40% of the sample, organic matter for 10%, and air and water fill about 50% of pore space. Soil develops under the combined influences of weathering and deposition.

Soil color shows how much organic matter, iron, magnesium and other minerals the soil contains. In most cases, the amount of organic matter dominates the soil color. Soils with high organic matter content are usually dark brown or black. Since organic matter helps create space between the mineral particles, brown or black soils often have good drainage. Organic matter also increases soil fertility and temperature stability. The presence of iron contributes to soil color by adding red, orange, or yellow tones.

Soil texture refers to the amounts and sizes of mineral particles. Minerals in soil result from weathering of bedrock and original material. It also results from the recombination of minerals as mineral-rich water runs through the soil. As you learned earlier, soil particles include sand (diameter of 0.05 mm to 2.0 mm), silt (diameter of 0.002 mm to 0.05 mm), and clay (diameter less than 0.002 mm). You can get a general idea about texture by rubbing the soil between your fingers. Sandy soils are rough and gritty, silty soils are less gritty, and clay soils are slippery or sticky.

The names of soils are often based on the proportions of three mineral sizes. A common soil texture is loam, which is composed of 5-27% clay, 28-50% silt, and 25-52% sand. Adding more clay, silt, or sand to these proportions can produce a clay loam, a silt loam, a sandy loam, etc. Soil texture often determines the use of the soil in agriculture. Soils containing a high amount of clay can drain slowly and may become waterlogged. The tightly packed clay particles slow down water movement and the small pore spaces hold on to the water. On the other hand, sandy soils drain rapidly because the large pore spaces around the minerals cannot hold water. Since they drain freely, they dry quickly.

Soils can be named using a soil texture triangle (Figure 2). The percentage size composition of the soil minerals has to be determined first in a mechanical analysis of settling or sieving. (An experienced soil scientist can make a good estimate using only his or her hands.) To use the triangle, locate the percent of sand along the bottom of the triangle. Follow from this point up and to the left, along the diagonal line. Then, locate the percent clay along the left side of the triangle and trace from that point straight across to the right. The textural class name for the soil is shown in the area where the sand and clay percentages cross. If your answer (where the sand and clay lines cross) ends up on a line dividing more than one section, you must give all possible names.

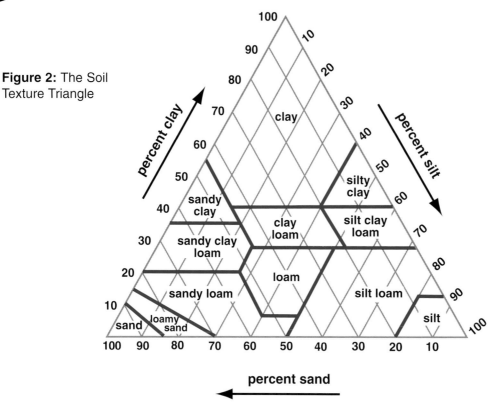

**Figure 2:** The Soil Texture Triangle

## Example

A mechanical analysis was performed on a soil sample and the following results were obtained: sand 45%, silt 40%, and clay 15%. Name this soil using the soil texture triangle.

*This soil should be classified as a loam.*

## Analysis Questions

1. Using your results from the mechanical analysis (Lesson 2: *Settling*, use the 24-hour reading), determine the textural classification of your soil sample.

2. Use the soil triangle above to classify the soil type for each sample below.

| Sample 1 | Sample 2 | Sample 3 | Sample 4 | Sample 5 |
|----------|----------|----------|----------|----------|
| 10% sand | 15% sand | 35% sand | 75% sand | 50% sand |
| 10% silt | 15% silt | 30% silt | 20% silt | 40% silt |
| 80% clay | 70% clay | 35% clay | 5% clay | 10% clay |

3. What component of soil is not included in the soil texture triangle? Explain how this might affect the texture of a soil sample.

4. Answer the essential question: *Explain how the soil texture triangle describes the texture of soils.*

# Lesson 3
# Organic Components

 *Driving Question:* What makes soil rich in nutrients?

## Overview

In the last lesson, you learned how the percentage of sand, silt, and clay in a soil sample determine its texture. There are other properties of soils that are not determined by texture. The amount of organic matter in the soil also determine some of its properties. In this lesson, you will investigate organic materials in soil. You will do chemical tests to determine which nutrients are contained in some soil samples. Finally, you will read about how farmers and gardeners can add nutrients to soil when they are needed.

## Important Content

- Organic material in soil can be: plant residue on the surface, very small, stable decayed material (humus), or live organisms.

- Adding organic material to the soil using peat or compost benefits soil by regulating water and airflow around plants, and by providing nutrients.

# Organic Components

 *Essential Question:* How is organic material related to the nitrogen in soils?

## Overview

You have learned that soil is made of minerals (in the form of sand, silt, and clay), organic material, and empty space (which can be filled with water or air). In this activity, you will investigate the organic material in soil.

The organic component of soil consists of raw plant residues, "active" organic material, and stable organic matter. Raw plant residues are plant materials that have not yet begun to decompose. They typically are found on the soil surface. Raw plant residues form a layer that protects soil from erosion by reducing the impact of raindrops, and by reducing the exposure of the soil to wind or water that can carry the soil away. The "active" organic material in soil is made up of decaying plant and animal matter, as well as live bacteria, fungi, mold, ants, earthworms, spiders, and other creatures. The life processes of these organisms make the soil more productive for growing plants. Active organic material releases nutrients into soil for use by growing plants, help keep soil porous, and hold solid soil particles together. They bind small soil particles into larger particles known as aggregates. This process, called aggregation, is important for good soil structure. The stable organic matter, also known as humus, is made of plant matter that has decomposed over time to create a material rich in carbon. Stable organic matter helps retain water, provides nutrients, and contributes to the soil's color. Farmers and gardeners value humus because it aids plant growth and increases soil water absorption.

In this activity, you will determine what organic materials are contained by several different soil samples. You will also test each soil sample to see how much nitrogen it contains. By comparing these two measurements, you will be able to answer the essential question: *How is organic material related to the nitrogen in soils?*

## Materials

5 soil samples
magnifying glass
distilled water
peat moss
eyedropper
filter paper
funnels
nitrate test paper
2 small jars

## Safety

Follow standard safety rules and school safety rules for laboratory activities.

## Procedure

1. Make a chart with columns for Color, Organic Material, and Nitrogen Content of each soil sample.

2. Generally, the blacker the soil, the more organic material it contains. Complete the Color column for each soil sample.

3. Do you see any other evidence of organic material in your soil samples? If so, describe what you see in the Organic Material column.

4. Measure out 30 mL of soil. Place 30 mL of the first soil sample in small jar. Add 30 mL of distilled water. Shake vigorously for 30 seconds.

5. Fold a circular piece of filter paper into a funnel and place it over the mouth of the jar.

6. Pour some of the soil solution into the funnel. Use the eyedropper to collect one drop of the water that filters into the jar.

7. Place one drop on the nitrate test strip. Wait 60 seconds, then record the concentration of nitrates in the soil.

8. Repeat for the other soil samples.

## Analysis Questions

1. Are dead leaves on the forest floor raw plant residues, "active" organic material, or stable organic matter?

2. Which of the soils had the highest concentration of nitrates?

3. Answer the essential question: *How is organic material related to the nitrogen in soils?*

# Peat and Fertilizer

 **Essential Question:** *In what three ways might plants benefit from the addition of peat moss or fertilizer?*

## Organic Material in Soil

Farmers and gardeners often add organic material to soil. This material adds needed nutrients, aids plant growth, and maintains plant health. Some of the main types of organic material added to soil are peat moss, mushroom compost, and bark. Sometimes, other organic and inorganic materials are added to these materials.

### What is fertilizer?

Fertilizer is any material that supplies one or more essential nutrients to plants. In other words, fertilizers are plant nutrients. Nutrients exist naturally in the soil, atmosphere, and in animal manure. However, naturally-occurring nutrients are not always available in the forms or quantities plants need. People then add these nutrients to soil by applying fertilizer, allowing optimum growth for plants.

Fertilizers can be classified into one of two categories: organic or inorganic. Organic fertilizers are derived from living or once-living materials. These materials include animal wastes, crop residues, compost, and other by-products of living organisms.

Inorganic fertilizers are derived from non-living sources and include human-made, or synthetic, commercial fertilizers. Synthetic and natural fertilizers contain the same ingredients, but synthetic fertilizers act more quickly. Synthetic fertilizers, however, also require energy or mining to produce, creating negative effects on the environment.

### Why do plants need fertilizer?

Plants require 17 nutrients for optimum growth—nine essential nutrients and eight micro-nutrients.

A nutrient is considered essential if plant growth and reproduction are greatly hindered in its absence.The essential plant nutrients are: carbon (C), hydrogen (H), oxygen (O), nitrogen (N), phosphorus (P), potassium (K), calcium (Ca), magnesium (Mg) and sulfur (S). These elements are needed in larger amounts by plants and are referred to as the macro-nutrients.

Iron (Fe), manganese (Mn), boron (B), molybdenum (Mo), copper (Cu), zinc (Zn), nickel (Ni) and chlorine (Cl) are needed in smaller amounts. They are referred to as the micro-nutrients, but they are also very important.

Sometimes the soil in a particular location does not contain enough of these nutrients for desirable plant growth or crop production. The nutrients in the soil can be used up by plants or washed away by water. Nitrogen, in particular, is a scarce resource in many soils. This is why

people often add fertilizer, for maximum plant productivity. Not all soils are the same and different plants have different nutritional needs. Both plant type and soil type must be considered when determining what fertilizer to use.

Live Sphagnum Moss

## Peat

Peat is one example of a fertilizer, Peat consists of partially decayed plants, especially mosses. Peat is formed in wetlands or bogs where plant matter decomposes slowly because of low temperatures or lack of oxygen. Because the plant matter decomposes slowly in those conditions, it accumulates faster than it can decompose. Peat is mostly composed of moss because mosses grow well under the conditions in which peat is formed, but it can also include grasses, sedges, and other organic debris.

Peat is classified according to its composition. The species of decomposed plants, the climate, and the site's water quality all help determine the type of peat. *Sphagnum* moss is the most common form of moss in peat. *Sphagnum* moss grows in cool northern regions and is often found in peat bogs in Washington, Maine, Minnesota, and Michigan.

Because it is so rich in organic matter, peat is often used as a fertilizer. Peat used for fertilizer is often called "peat moss." In addition to providing plants with nutrients, peat moss also helps soil hold water for use by plants. Moss leaves have many pores that retain water. When *sphagnum* peat is used as a growing medium for plants, as much as 93% of the water occupying this pore space is available to the plants. Even after it's drained, *sphagnum* peat can still contain 59% water and 25% air, by volume.

## Analysis Questions

1. In your own words, define "fertilizer." Why is fertilizer sometimes necessary? How does it help plants?

2. What is the difference between organic and inorganic fertilizers?

3. Intensive agriculture is planting the same field in crops year after year. How do you think this affects the need for fertilizer in the soil?

4. What is peat?

5. Answer the essential question: *In what three ways might plants benefit from the addition of peat moss or fertilizer?*

# The Nitrogen Cycle

 *Essential Question: How does nitrogen enter the soil?*

## Overview

Nitrogen is one of many nutrients plants need to grow. Nitrogen is the element that stimulates above-ground growth and produces the rich green color of a healthy plant. It also influences the quality of a plant's fruit and increases the fruit's protein content. Nitrogen, like other substances on Earth, passes through the atmosphere, soil, oceans and living things in a process that scientists call the *nitrogen cycle*. As it passes through the cycle, nitrogen can move from place to place and change forms. Farmers need to make sure that their plants have enough nitrogen to grow. So, they first understand where nitrogen comes from and how it might be brought to their plants.

## The Nitrogen Cycle

Free nitrogen ($N_2$) at normal temperatures is a gas. About 78% of the air you breathe is nitrogen. Nitrogen compounds are found in all fertile soils, in all living things, in foods, in coal, and in chemicals like ammonia. Nitrogen is also found in the nucleus of every living cell, as one of the chemical components of DNA.

Most of the nitrogen in the air and soil is not in a form that plants can use. Plants can only use nitrogen that is combined chemically with other elements in certain compounds, such as nitrate ($NO_3^-$), ammonium ($NH_4^+$) or nitrite ($NO_2^-$). Most nitrogen in soils is locked away in organic molecules, which plants cannot use. The chemical process of converting free nitrogen in the air and organic molecules in the soil into one of the compounds plants can use is called *nitrogen fixation*.

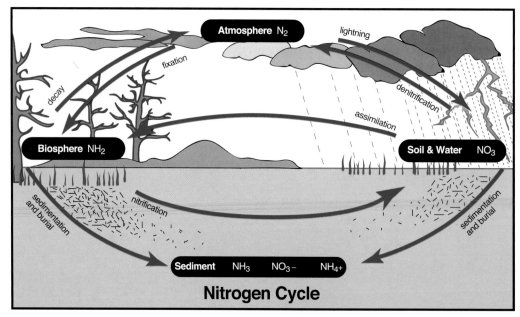

**Nitrogen Cycle**

A small amount of atmospheric nitrogen is fixed by lightning and by cyanobacteria (blue-green algae). However, most nitrogen fixation is performed by two kinds of soil bacteria: those that live free in the soil and those that live in the roots of certain plants like alfalfa, peas, beans, clover, soybeans, and peanuts. These plants are called legumes. More than 90% of *all* nitrogen fixation is performed by microorganisms that feed on the organic materials in the soil.

Nitrogen "fixed" as ammonium, nitrate, and nitrite is taken up directly by plants. It is incorporated in their tissues as proteins in a process called assimilation. The nitrogen then can be passed through the food chain from plants to herbivores to carnivores. When plants and animals die, they go through decomposition. In this process, bacteria or fungi break down large organic molecules like DNA, proteins, and carbohydrates into smaller molecules, including ammonium ($NH_4^+$). Bacteria then oxidize the ammonium to nitrite and other bacteria oxidize the nitrite to nitrate. The nitrate can then be taken up by green plants. This cycle of fixation-decay-nitrification-fixation can go on indefinitely without any nitrogen returning to a gaseous state.

Another group of microorganisms, the denitrifying bacteria, can reduce nitrate even further to molecular nitrogen ($N_2$). Denitrification occurs only in the absence of oxygen and is not common in well-aerated soils.

Nitrogen fixation can also be accomplished artificially. One practical way of adding nitrogen to soil is by growing legumes, so that the bacteria that live in their roots can fix nitrogen to the soil. Two other common methods include adding decomposing organic matter to soil or applying commercial nitrogen fertilizers.

## Analysis Questions

1. In what form is nitrogen most abundant?

2. What must occur for nitrogen to be taken up by growing plants? How does this process occur?

3. Answer the essential question: *How does nitrogen enter the soil?*

# Composting

 **Essential Question:** *How did your compost pile create organic material that could become part of soil?*

## Overview

Composting is the addition of organic material to any soil. The purpose is to enrich the soil by increasing the humus content. This provides an environment where earthworms and other organisms that break down organic material and aerate soils can survive. Natural composting occurs all over the world, as living things die and their remains decay and become part of the soil. Adding compost can help sandy soils retain water and improve drainage in clay-like soils. In sandy soils, compost decreases pore spaces. In clay-like soils, it increases the number of pore spaces around roots. Compost usually increases the abundance of nutrients available to plants (especially nitrate) and increases crop yield. In the past, farmers routinely performed composting as a way to improve soil. However, as inorganic fertilizers have become less expensive and easier to obtain, composting has become less common in large-scale agriculture.

In this activity, you will make a compost pile in your classroom or schoolyard. You will be able to observe the process by which organic material becomes part of the soil. Compost can be any organic material, including coffee grounds, fruit and vegetable wastes, egg shells, grass clippings, leaves, manure, pine needles, sawdust, and wood chips. Meat scraps, bones, eggs, cheese, oils, and grease generally should not be used in compost because they attract insects and other pests.

## Materials

1 large composting tub or plastic container
pitchfork, shovel, or large "barbecue" fork
vegetable peels and seeds
fruit peels and seeds
coffee grounds
egg shells
nut shells
any other vegetable or fruit scraps
hay or straw
grass clippings
leaves
ashes
sawdust
wood chips
weeds and other garden waste
sheep or cow manure (not dog, cat, or other carnivore)
shredded paper
soil or "ready" compost or compost "starter"
water

## Safety

Follow standard safety rules and school safety rules for laboratory activities.

## Procedure

1. Your compost pile will take several weeks to create. With your group, put together a plan to maintain your compost pile and observe what happens as the organic material decays.

2. Choose a container for making your compost. Any type of composting bin will do (chicken wire enclosure, wooden box, etc.). Place kitchen or yard wastes into the composting bin. Chop or shred the organic materials if you want them to compost quickly.

3. Spread soil, compost starter, or "already done" compost over the compost pile. This layer contains the microorganisms and soil animals that make the compost. It also helps keep the surface moist. The pile should be about 4 cubic feet in size.

4. Adjust the moisture in your compost pile. Add dry straw or sawdust to soggy materials or add some water to a pile that is too dry. The materials should be damp to the touch, but not so wet that drops come out when you squeeze it.

5. Allow the pile to sit and "cook." It should heat up on its own and reach the desired temperature (90 to 140 degrees F) in four to five days.

6. Each week, stir your compost, by turning it with a pitchfork, barbecue fork, or shovel. This will speed up the "cooking" time.

7. The pile will settle from its original height. This is a sign that the compost is "cooking" properly.

8. If you mix or turn your compost pile every week, it should be ready to use, in one to two months. If you do not turn it, the compost should be ready in about six to twelve months.

9. The best compost looks like dark, crumbly soil mixed with small pieces of organic material. It should have a sweet, earthy smell and be a rich, dark color. Feed compost to outdoor plants by mixing it with the soil.

## Analysis Questions

1. To make your compost pile, you added yard or kitchen waste. In the natural world, what would form compost?

2. To make your compost pile, you stirred the pile every week or so. In the natural world, what process would do this?

3. Answer the essential question: *How did your compost pile create organic material that could become part of soil?*

# Lesson 4

# Spaces in Soil

 *Driving Question: How does soil return and retain water?*

## Overview

So far, you have learned about what is in soil. Now you will explore what is not there. In this lesson, you will learn about the spaces in soil that can be filled with air or water. These spaces are very important because they determine how much air and water can get to the roots of plants. You will do two experiments in this lesson. In one, you will measure how much water can fit into those spaces in soil. In another, you will see how quickly water can flow through different soils with different spaces in them. You will use this information in the next lesson to calculate how much water plants can extract from each type of soil.

## Important Content

* The pore spaces in soil are important because they determine the amount of water available to plants living in the soil. The volume of these pore spaces is a function of soil type.

* The measurement of the total pore spaces in the soil is called porosity.

* Percolation (permeability) is the rate at which water can pass through soil.

# Estimating Porosity

 ***Essential Questions:*** *What is porosity? How does porosity affect the ability of soil to hold water?*

## Overview

Plants need three resources from the soil in order to grow. The first one is nutrients, which you learned about earlier in this chapter. Two other things that plants need from the soil are air and water. The tiny spaces between soil particles are very important for plant growth. They provide a space where soil can hold air and water that plants and other organisms can use.

Porosity is the term scientists use to describe the amount of open space in a sample of soil. The amount of open space in a soil is influenced by soil texture, ped size, ped shape, and compaction. A soil's porosity determines the total amount of water it can hold. The larger the volume of pore spaces in a soil, the higher its porosity and the more water it can hold. In this activity, you will investigate the porosity of several soil samples.

## Safety

Follow standard safety rules and school safety rules for laboratory activities.

## Materials

soil samples
water
plastic cup
250-mL graduated cylinder

## Procedure

1. Fill a plastic cup to 1 inch below the top with one type of soil. Do not pack down the soil.

2. Fill a 250-mL graduated cylinder with water. Slowly pour water into the soil, pausing frequently to let the water soak in and settle. Continue pouring until the soil can hold no more water. The soil can hold no more when the water begins to collect on the surface.

3. Make a data table and record the amount of water added to the soil type.

4. Repeat with the other soil samples.

## Analysis Questions

1. List the soil types in order by the amount of water you could add to the soil.

2. Which soil sample has the most space available to hold water?

3. In what situations might it be useful to know the water-holding capacity of a soil? Why?

4. Most farmers use heavy machinery like tractors, plows, and combines to work their fields. As these machines drive back and forth over a field, how would they affect the porosity of the soil? Explain your answer.

5. Answer the essential questions: *What is porosity? How does porosity affect the ability of soil to hold water?*

# Percolation

***Essential Questions:*** *What soil types have the fastest percolation rates? Which have the slowest rates?*

## Overview

As water enters and moves through a soil, it becomes available to the plant roots and animals which exist in that soil. The speed at which the water passes through the soil determines how long water remains in it. It also determines *how much* water the soil can retain for use by the soil organisms and plants. Many physical and chemical factors of the soil have an impact on how fast water moves through soil. However, it is not difficult to simply measure this speed in your soil samples.

In this exercise, you will determine the rate at which water moves through different types of soil. This rate is called the percolation rate, or permeability.

| Description | Percolation Rate |
|---|---|
| Very Slow | Less than 0.5 cm/hour |
| Slow | 0.5 to 1.6 cm/hour |
| Moderate | 1.6 to 5.0 cm/hour |
| Rapid | 5.1 to 16.0 cm/hour |
| Very Rapid | More than 16.1 cm/hour |

## Safety

Follow standard safety rules and school safety rules for laboratory activities.

## Materials

soil samples
250-mL graduated cylinder
grease pencil
ruler
stopwatch
for each soil sample, you will also need:
        container with small holes in the bottom (around 1 liter in size)
        500-mL beaker to place below the container

## Procedure

1. Collect your materials and bring them to your lab bench.

2. Add approximately 750 mL of one soil sample to the container with holes in the bottom.

3. Place the container on top of a 500-mL beaker with the drain hole pointing down. This beaker will catch the water that passes through the soil.

4. Use the grease pencil to make a mark 2.5 cm above the bottom of the catch beaker.

5. Create a data table with eight columns labeled: Soil Sample, Time Water Added, Time 2.5 cm Reached, Elapsed Time, Percolation Rate (cm/min), Time Until Finished, Total Volume of Water Returned (mL), Volume of Water Remaining in Soil (mL).

6. Slowly add 250 mL of water to each sample. Record on your data table the time when the water was added to the soil.

7. Allow the water to filter through the soil sample. On your data table, record the time when the water filled the catch beaker to the 2.5 cm line. Calculate the elapsed time between the time you first added the water and the time it reached the 2.5 cm line.

8. Allow the water to run until no more flows, or until it is dripping so slowly it appears to have stopped flowing. Some samples may drain so slowly it may be necessary to leave it for a while and check it later. Record the time that has elapsed since the water was first added to the soil and the time the water stopped flowing.

9. Measure and record the volume of the water returned to the catch beaker.

10. Calculate the percolation rate in cm/hour.

11. When all of the water has seeped through, you should notice that not all 250 mL of water has seeped out of the soil. Calculate the volume not returned and record it in the "Volume of Water Remaining in Soil (mL) column."

12. Share your group's data with the rest of the class.

## Analysis Questions

1. How do the rates for your sample compare to those of the scale in the overview? Indicate where all class samples fall on the percolation rate scale. (Remember to watch your units.)

2. What happened to the water that did not pass through your sample? Where is that water?

3. Which sample had the greatest holding capacity (capacity to retain water)?

4. How is holding capacity related to percolation rate? Write a hypothesis that you think explains this relationship.

5. Answer the essential questions: *What soil types have the fastest percolation rates? Which have the slowest rates?*

# Lesson 5
# Available Water

 *Driving Question: How much water can plants get out of the soil?*

## Overview

In the last lesson, you measured how much water soil can hold. This is important information, but it does not answer a crucial question. How much water can plants get from the soil? This lesson includes lab activities that will show you that not all water in the soil is available to plants. You will also read about the differences in available water based on the type of soil. Knowing how much water plants get from the soil helps determine the amount of water farmers need to grow crops.

## Important Content

- Available water is the amount of water available to plants. It is the amount of water between the wilting point and field capacity.

- Field capacity is the maximum amount of water that a field can hold without overflowing.

- The wilting point is the point at which no more water can be taken out of the soil by plants.

# Sponges

**Essential Question:** *Explain the difference between fields at the following levels of soil water: oven dry, permanent wilting point, field capacity, and saturation.*

## Overview

Soil is important because it anchors plants and provides them with nutrients and water. In this activity, you will learn how soil texture affects how much water is available for a farmer's crops.

Soil, as in a farmer's field, has four different stages: oven dry (a condition unlikely to occur in nature), permanent wilting point, field capacity, and saturation. In this activity, you will learn the differences between these stages. You will also calculate the available water for three different sponges, each representing a soil type.

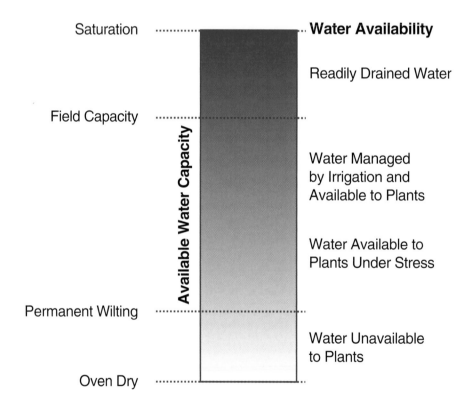

## Materials

3 oven-dry sponges of equal size
graduated cylinder
pie plate
500-mL beaker

## Safety

Follow standard safety rules and school safety rules for laboratory activities.

## Procedure

Do the following for each sponge.

1. Fill the beaker with 500 mL of water. This is already recorded for you in the Starting Water row on the data table.

2. Place an oven-dry sponge in the pie plate.

3. Pour water onto the sponge until the sponge has reached field capacity—the point at which water begins to flow out of the sponge. Use the sponge to soak up any water that is left in the pie plate. Determine the amount of water poured onto the sponge. Record this amount in the Field Capacity row on your data table.

4. Squeeze the sponge out into the pie plate until you cannot remove any more water. Measure the amount of water you squeezed out of the sponge. This is the amount of water that is available for plants. Record the number in the Available Water Capacity row in the table.

5. There is still water in the sponge, even though it cannot be squeezed out. This water is unavailable, and we say that the soil is at the wilting point, because plants that are in soil like this will wilt and die. Calculate how much water is left in the sponge, and record it in the Unavailable Water row in the table.

|  | Sponge 1 | Sponge 2 | Sponge 3 |
|---|---|---|---|
| Starting Water (mL) | 500 mL | 500 mL | 500 mL |
| Field Capacity (mL) |  |  |  |
| Available Water Capacity (mL) |  |  |  |
| Unavailable Water (mL) |  |  |  |

## Analysis Questions

1. Draw pictures to represent what a sponge looks like at oven dry, saturation, field capacity, and permanent wilting point.

2. How is the sponge you used in this activity similar to soil?

3. Answer the essential question: *Explain the difference between fields at the following levels of soil water: oven dry, permanent wilting point, field capacity, and saturation.*

# Soil Water Reservoirs

**?** ***Essential Question:*** *How does soil texture affect the available water capacity?*

## Overview

Read the following article and answer the analysis questions below.

## Water in Soil

Soil water is the water that is accessible to plants. It is held in the pore spaces between soil particles. The amount of water held in the soil after excess water has drained is called the *field capacity* of the soil. The amount of water in the soil is controlled by the soil texture, but other factors may influence it as well. A list of those factors is shown in Figure 3.

| Soil Property | Affect on Available Water |
|---|---|
| Texture | Primary determinant of available water due to particle size. |
| Rock fragments | Rock fragments take up space that otherwise could be held by water. |
| Organic matter | Organic matter absorbs water. Each 1% of organic matter increases the available water capacity by about 1.5%. |

**Figure 3:** Table of Factors That Influence Available Water Capacity

Soils composed mostly of clay-sized particles have more total pore space in a given volume than soils composed mostly of sand. As a result, fine-grained soils have higher field capacities than coarse-grained soils.

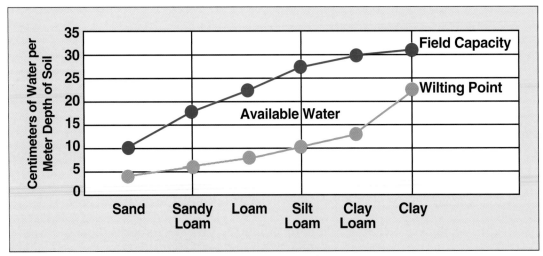

**Figure 2:** Relationship Between Available Water and Soil Texture

Figure 2 shows the relationship between soil texture, wilting point, field capacity, and available water. The difference between the wilting point and the field capacity is the available water.

Note that the coarsest soil, sand, has the smallest amount of available water. The amount of available water increases toward the center of the graph with loamy soils that have a mixture of different sized particles. The available water then drops off with the fine-textured soils on the right. How do we explain the relationship between available water and soil texture? Coarse soils do not have much available water because they do not hold much water to begin with. Low available water in fine soils results from the strong bonds between the clay particles and water. Plants have a harder time pulling the water away from the soil particles under these conditions.

## Analysis Questions

1. In Figure 2, the space between the line for field capacity and the line for wilting point represents the available water. Soil types with a large amount of available water have a large space between the lines. Soil types with a small amount of available water have a small space between the lines. Use Figure 2 to put the six soil types in order from most available water to least.

2. Is it true that soils with a high field capacity also have a large amount of available water? Why or why not?

3. Answer the essential question: *How does soil texture affect the available water capacity?*

Soil

# Wetlands

*Essential Question:* *What is a wetland and why is it important?*

## Overview

Read the following article and answer the Analysis Questions on page 50.

## Wetlands

Since it was first settled, the U.S. has lost about 50% of its wetlands. Most of this loss is the result of draining wetlands to make them useful for agriculture, real estate development, and other human uses. In California, about 90% of wetlands have been lost. To save what remains of these important ecosystems, federal and state governments have passed laws to preserve wetlands. One problem that has always confused wetland conservation is the issue of definition. What is a wetland? Is it land that is "temporarily" covered with water for part of the year? That leaves open the issue of what is "temporary." Landowners affected by efforts to preserve wetlands have argued over the definitions of these words. Today, scientists and governments use three factors to classify land as wetland:

**Water:** water must be present at or near the ground surface for a part of the year.

**Hydophylic plants:** most of the plants on the land must be adapted to wet conditions.

**Hydric soil:** the soil must have developed under wet conditions.

Many rare and common species rely on freshwater wetlands. Wetlands are complex ecosystems that can be very important to human life. Wetlands can regulate water flow by holding storm water for short periods and reducing floods. Wetlands can also purify water as it filters through by removing excess nutrients and pollution. Plants take up most of the nutrients that flow into a wetland. This prevents excess nutrients from flowing into bodies of water downstream where the extra nutrients could disrupt natural ecosystems. Many wetland plants also absorb pollutants, removing them from the water that flows out of a wetland.

Scientists call the way a wetland gets water, uses water, and releases water its hydrology. An important aspect of a wetland's hydrology is its water budget. A water budget is a way of accounting for the incoming and outgoing water in a system. In order to balance a water budget, a scientist must be able to identify all the water that comes in and goes out of a system in a specific period of time.

The water levels in a wetland vary with the seasons. This variation depends on the wetland's water budget and water-storage capacity. For example, if a region gets lots of rain or snowmelt in the spring, the area's wetlands will have a high water level during this season. If autumn in the same region is usually dry, the wetland water level is lower.

A wetland's storage capacity depends on the type of soil and rock beneath the wetland. Most wetlands occur in natural depressions in the land. The soil and rock underneath restrict drainage. A wetland's storage capacity naturally affects the volume of water it can hold. One wetland acre can store up to 360,000 gallons of water. Storage capacity is especially important during rainstorms. Healthy wetlands absorb huge amounts of storm water that might otherwise result in flooding.

Storage capacity determines the amount of time a given amount of water takes to move into, through, and out of a wetland. This is called a wetland's residence time. Residence time affects the extent to which a wetland removes nutrients and sediments from water. Wetlands with a long residence time are much better at purifying their waters than those with short residence times.

## Wetlands Restoration

Wetlands are an important part of the natural ecosystem in many places, including California. Scientists have estimated that 32% of California's endangered species are wetland species. Wetlands offer important benefits for water management. When carefully planned, restoration of wetlands can have a positive effect on wildlife, water quality, flood control, pollution control, and groundwater recharge.

The primary constraints on wetland restoration are cost and competing demands for the use of the land. Wetland restoration is relatively rare because the costs involved in restoring wetlands are often considered to be too high compared to the benefits. Restoration depends on the degree of wetland degradation and the economic value of the current land use.

There are three common types of wetland improvement:

**Wetland Restoration:** A degraded wetland or former wetland is returned to its previous condition as much as possible. This type of wetland improvement is the most likely to provide the desired benefits. One strategy for wetland restoration is called wetland mitigation. This involves minimal intervention and allows a wetland to regenerate itself naturally.

**Wetland Creation:** A non-wetland (dry land or non-vegetated water) is converted into a viable wetland. This is generally an expensive and difficult task.

**Wetland Enhancement:** One or more of the functions performed by a natural wetland are increased beyond those of the previous or current wetland. This is often a difficult task that may improve the functions of the wetland in its natural state. However, it also may diminish the wetland.

Before a wetland improvement project is started, the wetland must be studied to determine how degraded it is. A wetland that is only slightly degraded may not need much human help to restore itself. Any human activity that caused the degradation should certainly be stopped to permit the wetland to rejuvenate over time. For example, if a wetland has been mildly degraded by livestock grazing, then the livestock should be removed to restore the wetland, and the wetland should be given time to regenerate on its own.

The Environmental Protection Agency (EPA) recommends the following to guide any wetland improvement project.

1. Preserve and protect the aquatic environment. Retain as much as possible the natural features of the wetland.

2. Restore the wetland's ecological integrity. Maintain its natural community of plants and animals and remove invasive species.

3. Restore the wetland's natural structure and function such as size, shape, soil, rock, and other features.

4. Work within the watershed context. Maintain the wetland's function in terms of its place within the watershed. Also maintain its relationship to other water bodies, and inputs and outflows.

5. Address ongoing causes of degradation. To the greatest degree possible, eliminate factors that caused the degradation of the wetland.

6. Develop achievable goals, anticipate future changes, and design the wetland for sustainability. A wetland is a living ecosystem that is closely related to its changing environment. By restoring a wetland to its natural state, it should be healthy enough to weather future changes and sustain itself. It should not be required to deal with more human degradation, however.

7. Use passive restoration whenever possible. Less is more; do only as much as is needed to rid the wetland of the factors that degrade it. Give it time to restore itself; do not over-design or over-engineer the wetland.

8. Monitor the wetland to ensure that it is recovering. Make modifications as necessary.

As of 2004, there were more than 60 wetland restoration projects in Fresno County, California. One project in the Central Valley, on the Fresno River, is using wetlands' restoration to improve water quality. Other projects are removing invasive water hyacinths and restoring wetlands' flood-control functions. A project on Millerton Lake is restoring a wetland for wildlife habitat. A project in western Fresno County is removing salts from irrigation water entering groundwater and reducing soil erosion. Wetlands are also being restored along the San Joaquin River.

## Analysis Questions

1. What do scientists need to consider in classifying land as a wetland?

2. What is the difference between hydroperiod and residence time?

3. What are three ways a wetland can be restored?

4. Answer the essential question: *What is a wetland and why is it important?*

# Lesson 6
# Growing Fast Plants

 *Driving Question: What type of soil is the best for growing "fast plants"?*

## Overview

In this lesson, you will use what you have learned about soils to come up with a hypothesis. Your hypothesis will concern what type of soil provides the best environment for growing certain plants. You will conduct an experiment using "fast plants," or quickly growing plants, similar to cabbage. During the next several weeks, you will monitor how the plants grow and determine if your hypothesis was supported by evidence.

## Important Content

- The following variables are the primary ones that affect plant growth: amount of water, amount of sunlight, type of soil, temperature and climate.

# What Makes Fast Plants Grow?

 ***Essential Question:*** *In what conditions do fast plants grow best?*

## Overview

In this activity, you will plant a special kind of cabbage. Scientists know it as a "fast plant" because of the speed at which it grows. You will grow fast plants in special containers and under lights to make sure they have what they need to grow. You will use fast plants to learn more about how soil affects the way plants grow.

## Safety

Follow standard safety rules and school safety rules for laboratory activities.

## Procedure

In your group, devise an experiment to test one variable that could affect plant growth. Your experiment should involve growing some fast plants in different conditions. Be sure to describe the following:

- your hypothesis (what you think will happen)
- the variable you will change between plants
- the variables you will keep constant between plants
- a sample of the data table you will use to collect your data
- any changes you would make to the standard growing materials list
- any changes you would make to the standard growing procedure list (see following pages)

Share your procedure with the rest of the class. Be prepared to revise it based on the recommendations of other students.

## Analysis Questions

1. How does your experiment help to answer the essential question?

2. What is your prediction for the results of your experiment?

3. After you have collected your data from growing the plants, answer the essential question: *In what conditions do fast plants grow best?*

## Fast Plants: Standard Growing Materials

1 packet Wisconsin fast plant seeds
soil sample(s)
1 water mat
6 quads to hold four groups of plants
1 sheet diamond wicks
68 fertilizer pellets
1 water reservoir
2 pipettes

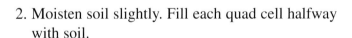

## Fast Plants: Standard Growing Procedure

Use this procedure to plant your fast plants in each type of soil. To start, you will grow a few seeds in each cell. Once the plants have begun to sprout, you will thin the "crop" to only one plant per cell. Each day, you will make observations of your plants. Once they are grown, you will harvest your plants and record the height and weight of your crop.

1. Drop one wick into each cell so that the tip extends halfway down the hole, about 2 cm.

2. Moisten soil slightly. Fill each quad cell halfway with soil.

3. Add 2 fertilizer pellets to each quad.

4. Fill each cell to the top with moistened soil.

5. Make shallow depressions on top of each cell. Do not press hard and compact soil.

6. Drop 2-3 seeds in each depression.

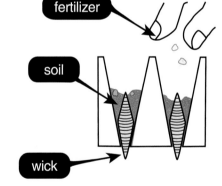

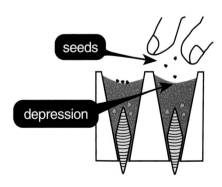

7. Sprinkle enough of the soil to cover seeds in each cell.

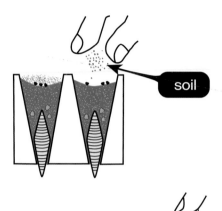

8. Water very gently with pipette or squirt bottle until water drips from each wick. Be careful not to wash seeds out of cells.

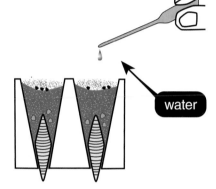

9. Label each quad with date and student's name. Place quads on water mat.

10. Position top of quad 5-10 cm below the light. Water from the top with squirt bottle for the first three days. Do not turn the light off while the plants are growing.

# The First Fast Plants

 *Essential Question: How were the first fast plants discovered?*

## Overview

Read the story and answer the analysis question.

## The Story of the First Fast Plants

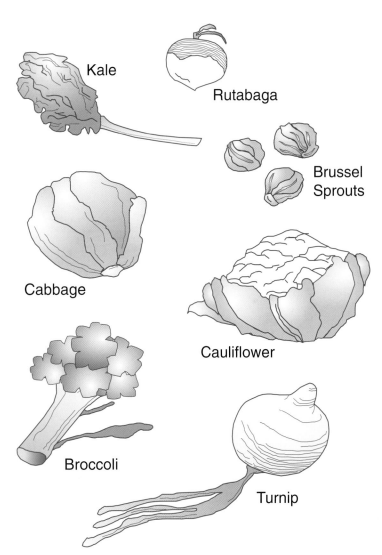

Many years ago, a farmer walked out to check on his barley field, planted on a rugged mountainside high in the Himalayas in Nepal. It was late spring. The snow had recently melted and the ground was becoming warm again. The barley he had planted a week earlier would provide grain to feed his family. The farmer just wanted to check the field. He did not expect to see any barley plants yet.

The farmer was astonished to see patches of sturdy, weedy brassica plants, growing in his barley field. He realized that these "weeds" must have sprouted very fast. The farmer thought a bit. It had been a long time since his family had had any fresh vegetables to eat. It would also be three months before the barley he had just planted could be harvested. So instead of destroying the weedy plants, he cut some and took them home for the family's supper.

In a few days, the farmer went back to his field. By this time, the little plants were producing bright yellow flowers. The farmer again took a few plants for his family to eat. The remaining plants attracted many hungry honeybees and soon produced pods with plump seeds.

The farmer picked the seeds and his wife pressed them for oil to use in cooking. The farmer wisely kept the rest of the seeds to plant the following year.

The next spring, the farmer scattered two types of seeds on his field, the brassica seeds and the barley. Both crops grew fairly quickly, but the weedy brassica plants came up first. They were already flowering while the barley was still spreading its shoots across the ground. The farmer harvested the brassicas before the barley was tall enough to shade them from the Sun. He was able to produce two crops on one piece of land. They provided enough food for his family and for the farm animals, the yaks, to eat.

Year after year, the farmer saved and replanted some of the brassica seeds. The little, weedy brassica was a relatively "primitive" plant that required no special fertilizer and was well adapted to survive on the mountainside.

Time passed. Soon the farmer's grandchildren were farming these same two crops on the terraced mountain field. So it continued, generation after generation.

One day early in the twentieth century, a plant expert and explorer from the other side of the world visited the mountainside farm in Nepal. When she saw the field of weedy little plants, she recognized them as a kind of brassica. She was familiar with the whole phylum of brassica plants. She knew that many brassicas are common vegetables, such as broccoli and various cabbages.

Since the little brassicas on the Nepalese farm had been grown for hundreds of years in the same location, they represented a unique plant stock. They were called a "land race," which would be genetically different from all other brassica plants everywhere. The plant expert knew the importance of preserving land races of plants. She collected some of the seeds from this brassica land race to take home to America. The seed was stored and saved by the U.S. Department of Agriculture's brassica seed collection at Iowa State University in Ames, Iowa.

The seed brought to Iowa by the plant expert remained in the seed storage collection for a long time. No one seemed particularly interested in it. Eventually, a plant scientist at the University of Wisconsin was seeking new genetic material for his research. He was interested in trying to breed vegetable brassicas like cabbage, broccoli, and turnips so they would not get diseases particular to brassicas. Scientists call plants that do not become diseased "disease resistant."

The scientist wrote to the curator of the brassica seed collection in Iowa and asked for samples of different kinds of seed of brassica land races. When they arrived, he planted them outside in his research plot. There, in the middle of the research plot, the little, weedy brassica from the mountainside of Nepal grew. This plant was about to connect the efforts of the observant farmer of long ago and the modern-day research scientist.

The scientist noticed the little brassicas right away because they flowered much quicker than any of the other brassicas. What value could a weedy little brassica be to his research? Standing there in the field, his thoughts raced. The plant did not look like much, but it flowered very early. The scientist knew that crossbreeding one cabbage type with another takes about a year, so the results of his research would likely be slow in coming. What if he could use this plant to develop a really fast flowering plant to test for disease resistance?

Like the farmer, the scientist decided to save the seed. He would grow the weedy brassica plants and their offspring under constant light and with only a small amount of soil, encouraging them to reproduce faster and faster. He would choose those plants that were shortest and sturdiest, that flowered the fastest, and that produced the most seed. He would then have a "model plant" he could use to crossbreed with disease-resistant brassicas. Eventually, he would transfer the disease resistance into his cabbages.

This is exactly what happened. The scientist called his model plants "fast plants." The little weedy brassica from Nepal was the great-great-grandmother of the fast plants. Today, scientists, students, and teachers are all working with fast plants. They are studying how plants grow and how they produce new generations of plants. Some students will become plant geneticists, molecular biologists, or plant breeders. They will write the next chapter in the story of the fast plants.

## Analysis Question

1. Answer the essential question: *How were the first fast plants discovered?*

# Thinning Fast Plants

## Overview

At first, your fast plants were grown in clusters to conserve space. Now, it is likely that several shoots are coming from each cell. In this activity, you will thin the cells down to one fast plant each.

## Safety

Follow standard safety rules and school safety rules for laboratory activities.

## Procedure

1. Observe each of your cells. If multiple fast plants are coming out of the soil, remove the smallest ones.

2. Record the number of shoots you removed in each quad on your data table.

## Analysis Question

1. If it is necessary to thin the fast plants after they have started to grow, why did we grow so many in the beginning?

# Harvesting Fast Plants

 ***Essential Question:*** *What were the results of your experiment and what conclusions did you draw from them?*

## Overview

It is harvest time! Your fast plants are ready to be harvested. Before the laboratory is cleaned up, you will need to take careful measurements of each of your fast plants to draw some conclusions about the experiment you did.

## Materials

centimeter ruler
electronic balance

## Safety

Follow standard safety rules and school safety rules for laboratory activities.

## Procedure

*Repeat the following steps for each fast plant.*

1. Remove the fast plants from under the grow lamp.

2. Gently hold the tallest leaf on your first fast plant and stretch it as high as you can without disturbing the soil. Use a centimeter ruler to measure the distance from the base of the soil to the leaf. Record the measurement on your data table.

3. Gently hold the plant right at the soil line. Slowly pull the plant out with your fingers, being careful not to break the roots or the leaves. With your hands, gently brush away as much soil as possible.

4. Put the plant—leaves, stem, and roots—on the balance and record its mass.

5. Discard the fast plant and clean up the quad as directed by your teacher.

## Write-Up

You now need to write up your experiment. Your write-up should include the following.

- a statement of the question you were trying to answer
- a description of the procedure you followed
- a table of your results
- a conclusion that analyzes the data and presents your findings
- an answer to the essential question: *What were the results of your experiment and what conclusions did you draw from them?*

# Agriculture

# Chapter 2
# Agriculture

## Connections

In the last chapter, you learned about soil and how it affects the amount of water that plants can use. In this chapter, you will learn more about agriculture and how farms manage water. By the end of the chapter, you will address one part of Fresno's water management problem – the use of water on crops. As you progress through the unit, you will learn about other aspects of the water conflict. In Chapter 6, you will be able to find a reasonable solution to Fresno's water problem.

## In this chapter:

This chapter allows you to use your knowledge of soils as they relate to entire farms. Since you cannot build a farm in the classroom, you will use computer programs to simulate a farm. The programs will help you calculate the water needs of crops and choose ways to bring extra water to farms. In the last chapter, you read angry statements from Fresno residents and environmentalists about how much water farmers waste every year. In this chapter, you will get a chance to see if there is any truth to those accusations.

## When you're done you'll be able to:

- Use precision farming methods to improve yield and water-use efficiency of a farm.

- Schedule appropriate irrigation for a specific crop and field location.

- Calculate the amount of water used by a given farm.

## Lesson 1

# Farming and Crops

 ***Driving Question:*** *Why is it important to understand the different methods for farming?*

## Overview

You will start to apply what you learned in the last chapter to understand how farms operate. You will compare the similarities between the plants you grew in class and those grown on the large farms that provide most of our food. You will read about the experiences in Lesson 1: *One Farm's Story*. You will also learn about hydroponic farming and organic farming, two increasingly popular ways of farming. In the next several lessons, you will learn about more connections between crops, soil, and water. These relationships are important to the problems that California and many other places are having with water availability.

## Important Content

- Organic farming grows crops without using artificial pesticides or fertilizers. It is more expensive to grow plants this way, but many consumers prefer them.

- Hydroponic farming grows crops without using soil. It is also more expensive to grow crops this way initially. However, crop growth and yield results can be controlled much more precisely by farmers.

# Thinking About Farms

***Essential Question:*** *How are our fast plants similar to and different from a farm?*

## Overview

In previous activities, you have learned about soil and how it affects plant growth. Farmers all over the world use their knowledge of plants and soil to grow crops that feed people. Do you think the plants you are growing in class are similar to those grown on farms? What are the similarities and differences between them?

## Discussion

Work with a small group to discuss the following questions. Take notes and be prepared to share your answers with the class.

1. Where is most of the food you eat grown?

2. How many days do you think it takes to grow corn from seed to harvest? How many days for tomatoes? How many for oranges? Explain how you arrived at your estimates.

3. What do you think it would be like to live on a farm? How would you spend your time? How would it be different from the way you live now?

4. How do you think farmers make decisions about what to grow, when to plant, and when and how much to water crops?

## Analysis Question

1. Answer the essential question: *How are our fast plants similar to and different from a farm?*

# One Farm's Story

**Essential Question:** *How did the Montiero family change its farming techniques and what resulted from these changes?*

## Overview

Below is a reading about a fictional farm that shows how farming is changing on a modern family farm. Read it and answer the analysis questions below.

In the reading, you will notice that the size of the farm is measured in hectares. A hectare is the area of a square 100 meters on each side, or about 2.4 acres. You can think of a hectare as a little larger than two football fields.

### Changing Farming Practices on the Montiero Family Farm

The Montiero family has farmed their California land for generations, producing profitable crops of tomatoes year after year. However, in 1993, Hector and his sons, Will and Eric, realized they were in trouble. Profits had been falling for years. If nothing were done to reverse the trend, they would likely lose the family farm within five years. Their concerns were well founded. On any drive around the area, the Montieros passed "For Sale" signs on what used to be their friends' and neighbors' farms. The farms were failing because traditional farming methods were no longer enough to make the farms profitable. The Montieros knew they needed to modernize their farming methods, but how?

Hector started his search for solutions at a conference he read about in a farm journal. At the conference, he learned new information about compost, calcium-magnesium ratios, and other new methods and technologies he had never heard of. He asked questions, bought books, and brought consultants back to his farm. Hector was astonished at what they found.

"They told me that my soil didn't have the right nutrients for tomatoes," Hector said. This realization was a turning point in his farming methods. After much careful study, the Montieros adopted a "systems approach" to farming their land. A systems approach is when farmers look at all the parts of farming as a system. They look at the current state of water and nutrients in the soil, the types of crops they have planted, and historical data on precipitation. The Montieros looked at all those factors. Then, they could make decisions on what to plant, and how much to irrigate and fertilize by looking at what they were putting in the 'system', what reserves the system already has, and what comes out of the system.

Hector and his sons learned that they would get the best yields if they gave their land a rest in some years. They decided to plant soybeans, which fix nitrogen in the soil, on one part of the field each year. Today, leafy bean plants cover 25% of the Montiero farm. The beans not only enrich the soil but also bring in $4.50 a bushel. This is not much, but it is a better deal than depleting the soil year after year. After the harvest, the bean vines are plowed under for on-the-spot composting, reducing the need for the commercial fertilizers they used to add every year.

What has been the outcome after all these changes? The Montieros have greatly improved the quality of their soil. They have achieved a 25% increase in yield and a 20% decrease in total input costs since they made the changes. The investments they made in their new approach to farming have paid off, both in terms of soil health and profits. Before the transition, the Montieros spent $175 to $200 per hectare on fertilizer. After making the changes, Hector's fertilizer expenses were down to $100 per hectare. Because his yield has increased even though they use less fertilizer, Hector and his sons now plan to cut fertilizer applications by another $25 per hectare next year. This will result in a farm-wide savings of $60,000. Even with cost-cutting measures, yields have increased from about 35 tons of tomatoes per hectare before the transition to an average of 60 tons per hectare in 2005.

Despite all these changes, some things remain the same. About farming, Hector says, "It's not just a living, it's our soul. My ancestors risked everything they had to build up this farm for our family. I'm determined to keep it going." The concept of a healthy family farm is important to Hector. Farm failure was simply not an option for the Montieros. "My family's been farming for 150 years, and I wasn't going to let the farm go down on my watch," Hector says.

No more major changes are planned at the Montiero farm. They will continue building the soil quality and reducing artificial fertilizer inputs whenever possible. For now, it appears the changes made by Hector should preserve the Montiero farming tradition for generations to come.

## Analysis Questions

1. What had been happening to the farms in this area?

2. Draw a diagram of the Montiero farm system that shows the inputs and outs, and how they are related. Use boxes for inputs and outs and arrows for relationships. Be sure to label them.

3. Answer the essential question: *How did the Montiero family change their farming techniques, and what resulted from these changes?*

# Hydroponic Farming

***Essential Question:*** *How is hydroponic farming different from growing "fast plants" in our classroom?*

## Overview

Read the following article about hydroponic farming and answer the analysis questions below.

## Hydroponic Farming

Do you think it is possible for plants to grow without soil? You may find this hard to believe, but most plants can. Scientists have found that plants do not necessarily need soil for growth but do require the nutrients that they usually get from the soil.

If plants do not need soil, then why do plants grown so well in soil? Soil provides support materials for the plant's roots. It also acts as a nutrient reservoir for the plant. The plant takes up the nutrients in the soil, which it uses for growth and cellular repair. Soil provides nutrients and structural support for plants.

Scientists have found ways to provide nutrients and support to plants without using soil. This method of growing plants is called hydroponic farming. In greenhouses that use hydroponic farming, they use a substance similar to soil that is called a medium. The medium is usually made up of material that can help support the plant and hold water and nutrients.

There are a number of different growing media to choose from. Two of the most popular growing media are heydite (small pieces of shale rock) and rockwool (melted rock spun like cotton-candy). Some of the other common media are expanded clay, coco coir, perlite, vermiculite, and oasis root cubes. Expanded clay is small baked pebbles of clay. It can be reused if cleaned and cared for properly. It works well for growing plants because it has lots of pore space for water, air, and nutrients. Coco coir comes for coconut husks and tends to have high salt contents. Perlite is a volcanic rock that can hold a lot of air but not a lot of water. Vermiculite is like perlite but holds more air. Oasis root cubes are foam cubes with fertilizer. They are convenient because they come in lots of different pre-cut sizes and have pre-punched holes for inserting plants or seeds. All of these media have certain advantages and are better for some plants than for others.

While plants can grow without soil, plants still need air, water, light, and nutrients. At outdoor hydroponic farms, air and light are available naturally. At indoor hydroponic farms, a circulation system gets air to plants, and artificial light from lamps supplement the natural light plants receive. Both kinds of hydroponic farming require adding water and nutrients to the growing media. Nutrients are added with fertilizers specially designed for hydroponic growing systems. A plant's nutrient needs change depending on its stage of development. That means it is important for farmers to frequently change the nutrient solution they are applying. If a plant does not receive the proper nutrients, it affects the plants health and growth. For example, nitrogen and phosphorous are both essential for plants to thrive. If a plant does not get enough of these nutrients its color changes, its lower leaves may turn yellow, and it will stunt the plant's growth. Deficiencies of other nutrients can cause other problems. The leaves of plants that do not have enough potassium or zinc start to look papery, and the leaves of plants without enough copper curl. Because air, water, light, and nutrient variables are all controlled, hydroponic farming is sometimes also called "controlled environment agriculture." Almost any plant will grow in a hydroponic environment as long as these variables are adapted to each plant, but some grow better than others.

Hydroponic farming has been around for thousands of years. Today, this technology is used to grow healthy indoor plants, vegetables, fruits, and herbs. One advantage of this type of farming is that many hydroponic plants yield more vegetables in less time than the same plants grown in soil. Hydroponic farming can also be useful in colder regions, where long winters limit the length of a growing season and the quantity of plants that can be grown in a year. However, hydroponic farming in a colder climate requires the use of an energy source other than direct sunlight for heating and photosynthesis.

One of the reasons California farming is so successful is the state's long growing season and climate. If farms in other regions could start producing more crops with hydroponic growing methods, it might reduce the nation's dependency on California for produce and take the stress off of California's water resources. Hydroponic farming could also be useful to California farmers. Since all the growing variables are so carefully controlled, farmers would only have to use the exact amount of water they need for their crops. Given the concerns over the depletion of California's water supply, hydroponic farming could be one way of conserving resources.

## Analysis Questions

1. In your own words, define hydroponic farming.

2. What needs of a plant must be met for it to grow well?

3. Write a hypothesis about what kinds of food plants would be easiest to grow with hydroponic methods. Explain your choices.

4. Increasing hydroponic farming in areas with plentiful freshwater would decrease the demand for water in California. What resources would it require in the new location?

5. Answer the essential question: *How is hydroponic farming different from growing "fast plants" in our classroom?*

# Organic Farming

**Essential Question:** *How is organic farming different from growing "fast plants" in our classroom?*

## Overview

Have you ever heard the term organic? You may have seen it on food packages or in the produce isle. Foods that are labeled as organic have been grown or produced without using any human-made or artificial materials. In the reading below, you will learn more about what organic farming is and how farmers can grow crops organically.

### Organic Farming

Most farmers use human-made products to protect their crops and help them grow. These products mostly fall into three categories: fertilizers, pesticides, and herbicides. Fertilizers provide nutrients that help crops grow. Pesticides prevent insects and other "pests" from damaging the plants. Herbicides prevent weeds that could interfere with the growth of crops from growing. Many of these products include substances that do not occur in nature. Any product that contains substances that do not occur in nature is called *artificial*.

Farmers who use organic methods to not use any artificial fertilizers, pesticides, or herbicides. Instead, they use other methods to protect their crops and help them grown.

### How do Organic Farmers Protect Their Crops?

One of the principles of organic farming is to be proactive instead of reactive. This means taking preventative measures to protect their crops from pests and disease. They use methods to keep pests and diseases away from their crops before the pests and diseases become a problem.

Farmers know that pests prefer weak or diseased plants to healthier ones. That means farmers want ways of growing the healthiest plants possible. But how can farmers ensure the health of their crop? One thing plants need is healthy soil. So how can farmers make their soil healthy? Organic farmers use natural methods like cover crops and crop rotation to enhance soil quality. Cover crops are plants farmers can grow during the times they are not growing their regular crops. Cover crops add extra nutrients to the soil. Crop rotation helps crops in the same way. Crop rotation is when farmers periodically change the crop they grow. For example, a farmer might plant corn for a few years and then plant soybeans for a year. Each crop takes different amounts and kinds of nutrients from the soil. By planting different crops instead of the same one over and over again, farmers get a healthier soil with more nutrients. Having healthy soil creates healthy plants, which are better able to resist disease and infection. Healthier plants means fewer unwanted pests.

Having healthy plants is not all it takes to keep pests away, though. Organic farmers also rely on different soil organisms, insects, and birds to control pest problems. Predators, such as birds and bats, eat insects that hurt farmers' crops. Farmers can also buy and release helpful insects

into their fields, like ladybird beetles, who eat aphids (insects that suck sap out of plants and trees) and other pests.

Even though having healthy soil and using predators to eat pests can be helpful, sometimes it is not enough to keep pests away. When pest problems get out of control, farmers have other organic methods they can use. One method is called mating disruption. Like the name suggests, this is when farmers take steps to stop pests from reproducing. For instance, farmers can stop moths from mating by hanging decoys that smell like female moths. The male moths get confused and cannot find female moths to mate with. As a result, the moths cannot produce baby larvae, which destroy crops. Farmers can also use traps and barriers to protect their crops from pests. A simple trap is to bury cups filled with soapy water. Insects walking along the ground fall in the soapy water and get stuck. Planting barriers around a field can also protect crops. The barrier can keep good soil in the field and keep chemicals from other fields out. Helpful insects that eat pests also like to live in these barriers. As a last resort, farmers can carefully apply naturally occurring pesticides to their crops.

Pest control is only one problem organic farmers face. Organic farmers are also concerned with how weeds affect their crops. But they have to protect their crops from weeds without using chemical herbicides. One method they use is to control weeds through increased cultivation. This means loosening soil around growing plants, which removes the weeds. Other methods include using mulches and flame weeding. Mulch is a protective covering. It fills in spaces between plants, which makes it difficult for weeds to break through the surface and grow. Flame weeding is a process that kills small weeds by passing fire over them. The weeds are never set on fire, but the intense heat makes it impossible for the weed seedlings to survive. These and other methods give organic farmers a way to grow produce without using any unnatural materials or chemicals.

### Why Organic?

These methods take a lot more work and cost more than other farming methods, which results in organic produce being more expensive. Many people are willing to pay extra for fruits and vegetables grown without chemicals. They believe the organic food is safer for their families and the environment. There is evidence that artificial chemicals and fertilizers are harmful to the environment. When farmers spray or use artificial chemicals on their crops, some of the chemicals get into the soil and seep into the water supply. These chemicals could be toxic to other plants and animals that rely on the water. Artificial fertilizers can cause problems, too. If they wash off the fields into streams, lakes and ponds, they can upset the ecosystem's balance by contributing to the growth of certain organisms at the expense of others. It is because of these risks that some people find organic farming methods and produce appealing.

## Analysis Questions

1. In your own words, define "organic farming."

2. Answer the essential question: *How is organic farming different from growing "fast plants" in our classroom?*

## Lesson 2
# Evapotranspiration

*Driving Question: How much water do plants need on a farm?*

## Overview

In this lesson, you are going to learn about agriculture and water use. You have already learned how soil affects growing plants. You have seen some of the ways that soil and water interact and how water moves from soil into plants. You know that water enters the soil mainly from rain or artificial irrigation systems. But how does water leave the soil? How much water do plants take out of the soil? You will conduct two experiments in this lesson. One will look at evaporation of water from the surface of soil. Another will look at how much water plants use, on average, every day. You will then read about *evapotranspiration*, the measurement farmers use to determine the amount of water their crops need.

## Important Content

- Plants use water through the process of transpiration.

- Evapotranspiration is the combined total of evaporation and transpiration from a field. This varies by soil, crop type, plant size, and environmental factors.

- Evapotranspiration is used to determine how much water crops need.

# Evaporation

 *Essential Question: How can people minimize water losses due to evaporation?*

## Overview

In this activity, you will measure the rate of evaporation of water in a container. You will choose the location of your container and predict how your evaporation rate compares with those of other students in your class.

This activity is divided into two parts. You will do the first part in class today and the second part in a few days.

## Materials

*For each group of students:*

• container with straight sides

• 100 mL graduated cylinder

• water

## Safety

Follow standard safety rules and school safety rules for laboratory activities.

## Procedure/Part 1

1. Choose a container to put your water in. Use the graduated cylinder to measure exactly 100 mL of water. Pour the water into your container.

2. Choose a location for the container where other students will not disturb or move it for one full week. Describe the location you chose in your notebook.

## Analysis Questions/Part 1

1. Describe the size and shape of the container you put the water in.

2. Describe the location where you placed the container.

3. How much of the water do you predict will evaporate before class tomorrow? What reasoning led you to make this prediction?

4. Look at the containers and locations that your classmates have chosen. Do you think they will lose more or less water due to evaporation? Why?

## Procedure/Part 2

Do Steps 1 and 2 below each day for the next week.

1. Record the amount of water remaining in your container by carefully pouring it into the graduated cylinder.

2. Calculate and record the amount of water you lost to evaporation.

3. At the end of the week, make a graph of your data. Put the day on the x-axis and the amount of water in your container (in mL) on the y-axis.

## Analysis Questions/Part 2

1. Which container in your class lost the most water? Why?

2. What factors might cause water to evaporate quickly?

3. How do you think evaporation would compare in California (a hot, windy state) with Washington (a mild, rainy state)?

4. Answer the essential question: *How can people minimize water losses due to evaporation?*

# Transpiration

 ***Essential Question:*** *What factors affect the amount of water a plant uses?*

## Overview

Water is one of the basic substances that plants require to live. In fact, most of the weight of a plant is water. In plants, more than 90 percent of the water taken in by the root system evaporates into the air through holes in the surface of leave. This loss of water through the leaves is called **transpiration**. A mature corn plant transpires about 15 liters of water per week.

As water evaporates from leaves, it is replaced in the plant by water drawn up from the roots through the stem. Tiny pores called stomata, located on the underside of leaves in most plants, open and close in response to environmental conditions, including the humidity of the air, the amount of light available to the plant, carbon dioxide concentrations in the air, and the water content in plant tissue. For example, wind increases transpiration while high humidity reduces transpiration. High temperatures tend to increase transpiration although plants often close their stomata when it is extremely hot and dry. Open stomata are very important for a plant. It is through these pores that carbon dioxide enters the plant to be converted by photosynthesis into food for the plant.

In this activity, you will conduct an experiment to measure the transpiration of different plants.

## Materials

*For each lab group:*

- 4 test tubes
- 4 corks or stoppers with holes (clay will also work well)
- 4 plant cuttings
- large graduated cylinder
- water
- fan
- grease pencil

## Safety

Follow standard safety rules and school safety rules for laboratory activities.

## Procedure: Set Up

1. Cut four stems of similar size from your plants. Two of the stems should contain one healthy leaf each. The other two stems should contain three or four healthy leaves of approximately the same size (leaf surface area).

2. Carefully cut the end off the stem while it's under water to prevent air pockets from forming in the stem.

3. Insert the stems through the holes in the stoppers. Use modeling clay to seal the hole, as shown below.

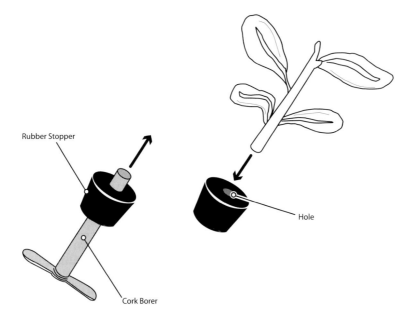

Rubber Stopper

Cork Borer

Hole

4. Insert the stopper with the stem into a test tube that is 3/4 full of water. The stem should be well below the water line.

5. For all four plants, mark the water level on the test tube with a grease pencil.

6. Place two of the stems (one with one leaf, the other with multiple leaves) in front of a fan operating at a low setting. Place the other two stems in the same environment, but away from the fan. Make sure all plants are receiving adequate light.

7. Make a data table to record the height of water each day and the general health of the plant stem. Record your observations for the first day.

8. Complete the first three Analysis Questions.

## Procedure: Ongoing Observations

1. Record the water level daily by using a ruler to measure the distance from the mark you made to the new water level.

2. Graph your results, putting the time (days) on the x-axis and the water height (cm) on the y-axis. Be prepared to share your results with your classmates.

3. Answer the remaining Analysis Questions.

## Analysis Questions

1. In your own words, define *transpiration*.

2. Which stem do you think will use the most water over the next week? Why?

3. Why did you seal the hole in the stopper with clay?

4. Which stem used the most water? Which used the least?

5. How do your results compare with those of your classmates? Do you see any patterns in the data?

6. Answer the essential question: *What factors affect the amount of water a plant uses?*

# Evapotranspiration

*Essential Question: Why is it crucial for farmers to understand evapotranspiration?*

## Overview

Read the following article and answer the Analysis Questions that follow.

You have learned about evaporation as the process of water exposed to air becoming water vapor and entering the air. You have also learned about transpiration, where plants release water into the air through evaporation. If we add those two ideas together, what do you think evapotranspiration means? Why do you think farmers would need to understand this process?

### Plants and water use

We know that water is important for plant growth. We also know that plants take up their water from the soil through their roots. But how does water move up the plant?

Plant uptake of water is controlled by the *water potential gradient.* Water potential gradient is the measure of how much water is available in the plant and out of the plant. For example, if there is a large amount of water in the soil and a low amount of water in the plant, water absorbed by the roots gets pushed up through the plant. The water travels through a system of tissues called the *xylem.* Xylem provides a path for water to travel to all the individual cells in the plant. The plant uses the water in many ways. Water can carry nutrients from the soil to plant cells, it can cool the plant, and it helps the plant stand upright. When plants are wilted, it is usually because their cells lack water. Water prevents wilting by filling in the cells and causes the plant to become rigid.

Water is also important for photosynthesis. In photosynthesis, plant cells use the energy in sunlight to combine carbon dioxide and water to form a sugar. This sugar is a type of fuel that stores energy absorbed from the sun. Plants break down sugars to get energy to perform daily functions such as growing, and opening and closing stomata. The breakdown of sugar also provides building materials that the plant can use for growth and repair of cells and tissues.

Water is essential for photosynthesis, but this is not the only thing plants use water for. Less than 10% of the water absorbed by a plant is retained in the cells or used in photosynthesis. Plants also use water as a cooling agent. Ninety percent of more of the water absorbed by a plant is released through transpiration. This evaporation or water through stomata cools the plant in the same way that sweat evaporating from our skin helps cool our bodies.

### What is evapotranspiration?

Evapotranspiration, or ET, is the transfer of water to the atmosphere due to evaporation from the ground and transpiration through plants. The term "evapotranspiration" combines the words "evaporation" and "transpiration." Its meaning also combines the two processes. When scientists measure the rate of evapotranspiration, they are measuring the water evaporating from the surface of soil and the transpiration of the plant.

Since plants take water from the soil, evapotranspiration is the total water transfer from the soil to the air. Therefore, ET is sometimes called crop water use. When seedlings are young and small, water mostly enters the air through evaporation from the soil. This is because the surface of the soil is exposed to the air and the plants have few leaves. As plants grow, their leaves shade the soil and reduce soil evaporation. The plants now become the major contributor of water evaporating into the air through transpiration from leaves.

To provide enough water to a crop successfully, a farmer needs to know how ET is occurring at any given time.

## Weather conditions affects ET

Moisture and temperature are two conditions that affect how much water evaporates from the soil and how much water plants transpire. Hot, dry, sunny weather increases ET. When it is very hot the stomata open, and the plant may lose too much water to transpiration. In cold weather, the stomata tend to close. In dry weather, some plants are more likely than others to close most of their stomata to prevent water loss. This reduces the amount of water entering the air. When the soil is wet and the plant has lots of water, stomata open to release water.

Additionally, most plants open their stomata during the day, when it is light. That way they can take in the carbon dioxide they need for photosynthesis. At night, stomata close, so less transpiration occurs. (This is not true of cacti and some other desert plants that keep their stomata closed during the day and open at night. Can you guess why?)

Wind is another key factor. The stronger the wind, the greater the ET. Strong winds blowing over exposed soil increase evaporation from the ground. Strong winds also pull water away from plants faster. To calculate ET correctly, farmers must understand how their particular crop reacts in different weather conditions.

## ET changes as the crop grows

Different types of plants are capable of moving water at different rates. Even the same crop may have very different water-use rates. It depends on the plant's stage of growth, the number of leaves on the plant, and their surface area. Farmers use these variables to determine a number called the "crop coefficient." The crop coefficient shows how the ET of one crop compares with the ET of a reference crop. For example, alfalfa is often used as a reference crop; ET for a full canopy of alfalfa is called "reference ET." A crop coefficient multiplied by the reference ET gives the crop's ET. Thus, if a reference ET is known, farmers can use crop coefficients for any crop to quickly estimate its ET. Then, the farmer knows how to calculate how much water a crop will require.

### *Summary*

- Evapotranspiration, or ET, is a term that describes the transfer of water to the air from both plants and soils. Another term for ET is crop water use.

- Plants need water to meet their ET requirements. If ET demand is not met, crop growth and yield suffer. ET is an important factor in determining how much water plants need.

- Weather conditions determine how fast water evaporates from a crop. Different crops may have a different ET for the same weather conditions.

- ET can be determined daily to help farmers make the right water use decisions.

## Analysis Questions

1. How do plants absorb water from the soil? How do they transfer it to the air?

2. What part of plant roots is involved in water absorption? How does water get from the roots to all the plant's cells?

3. Define evapotranspiration.

4. How does weather affect evapotranspiration?

5. Answer the essential question: *Why is it crucial for farmers to understand evapotranspiration?*

# Hydro—The Water Molecule

 ***Essential Question:*** *How many paths can one drop of water take during its lifetime?*

## Overview

In the last several activities, you have learned how water moves through plants and the soil. This water movement, called evapotranspiration, is only a part of the many ways water moves through the environment. Water moves all over the Earth in the water cycle. The cycle is a never-ending variety of paths from the oceans, to the atmosphere, back to the soil and the plants that need it.

Today, you will meet "Hydro," a water molecule whose life on Earth you will follow. You will get a chance to map Hydro's virtual journey through the water cycle.

## Materials

computer with Hydro website

25 index cards

30 index cards with arrows

Water Transformation Data Table

## Procedure

Your task is to make a map that shows Hydro's entire journey. Follow these directions to make your map.

1. Open the file "hydro.htm." Navigation from page to page will depend on choices that are made at each location in Hydro's journey. [**Important Note:** movement is only in one direction—forward. Using the web browser's **Back** button is not allowed.]

2. As you read each page, look for any terms that are in color. Red words refer to residences or places that Hydro stays during the journey. Scientists call these resting places *reservoirs*. When you come across a red word, **write it down on an index card**.

3. Blue words refer to transformations that Hydro undergoes in getting from one reservoir to the next. **Draw an arrow on a separate index card and label it with one of these words.**

4. Record the definition of each transformation on the Water Transformation Data Table.

5. As you proceed through Hydro's journey, place the index cards on the table to form the connected patterns you observe.

6. Each time you find a red or blue word, create a new card. However, when you find a red word that you have already seen on Hydro's journey, do not create a new card for it. Instead, use the arrows to connect the current reservoir to the previously used red term.

7. It will be necessary to move through Hydro's journey many times to discover how all parts of the journey are interconnected. That is the nature of a complex cycle with many pathways. Remember, going backwards through the web pages is not allowed!

## Water Transformation Data Table

As you go through Hydro's journey, write down the transformations (blue words) and their definitions.

| Transformation | Definition |
|---|---|
| Infiltration | |
| Groundwater Flow | |
| Evaporation | |
| Condensation | |
| Sublimation | |
| Precipitation | |

## Analysis Questions

1. On a sheet of paper, draw all the reservoirs and transformations of Hydro's journey.

2. Normally, you can use the **Back** button when using a web browser. Why couldn't you use this feature during Hydro's journey?

3. Where does evapotranspiration occur in the water cycle (in Hydro's journey)?

4. Answer the essential question: *How many paths can one drop of water take during its lifetime?*

# Understanding Hydro

 ***Essential Question:*** *What is the hydrologic cycle?*

## Overview

Congratulations! Hydro's journey is now complete. In the real world, scientists refer to this journey as the hydrologic cycle (the water cycle). Cycles are processes that do not have a beginning or an end, and the same repeated stages are predictable and periodical. In this lesson, you will make a poster of the hydrologic cycle. While you are making your poster, think about how the many parts of the water cycle affect farms and plants, and the water they can use.

## Materials

large sheet of poster board or butcher paper

markers or colored pencils

sketch of "Hydro's" Journey

computers (if needed)

## Procedure

1. Create a poster of Hydro's journey based on the sketch you made in Lesson 2: Agriculture.

2. As you draw, keep in mind that:
   • Every reservoir (area of storage) should be connected by at least two arrows.
   • All arrows should represent a transformation (action).

3. Use the computer if necessary to check the definition of terms that remain unclear.

## Analysis Questions

1. Starting in the soil, summarize Hydro's journey through a plant and back to the ocean. Use at least 5 steps.

2. How is it possible for several arrows to connect to one reservoir?

3. Answer the essential question in your own words: *What is the hydrologic cycle?*

## Lesson 3

# Crop Types

**Driving Question:** *How do different crops use water?*

## Overview

In the last lesson, you saw how plants use water. You also saw that plants of different sizes use different amounts of water. Do you think this is also true of different kinds of plants? In this lesson, you will study the water requirements of different plants. You will also analyze graphs of their water use in different seasons throughout the year. Seasons are very important in agriculture because rain only comes at certain times of the year. Hopefully, the rainfall comes at the right time for the plants. If the rain does not come, or if there is not enough rainwater to support the plants, farmers must add water to the fields through irrigation. If they do not irrigate, crop growth will suffer because of a condition called drought, which you will study in the next several lessons. Irrigation is not always an option. Sometimes, there is no available water source nearby, and sometimes it is simply not economical to pump water to the field.

## Important Content

- Evapotranspiration varies by crop type, plant size, and life cycle stage.

# Corn and Water Use

 *Essential Question: At what stage of its life would a corn plant need the most water?*

## Overview

In this activity, you will think about how plants grow and how they use water during their growth cycle. Corn plants are one of the most demanding crops in terms of water usage, and they have a life span from 90 to 150 days. Think back to what you learned in the last lesson about evaporation and transpiration as you answer the analysis questions.

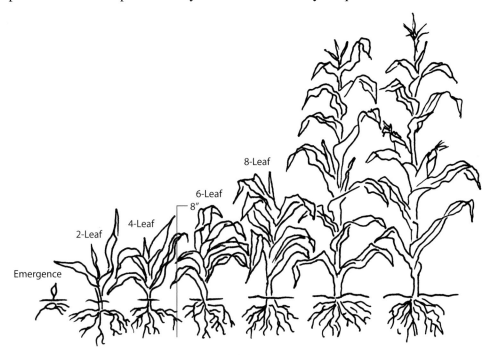

## Analysis Questions

1. Describe the size and shape of a corn plant at the beginning, middle, and end of its life. How is it alike? How is it different?

2. Describe how you think the water needs of a corn plant would change over its life span, based on what you learned in the last lesson.

3. Answer the essential question: *At what stage of its life would a corn plant need the most water?*

# Crops in California

*Essential Question:* What can you learn from an evapotranspiration graph?

## Overview

When farmers look at evapotranspiration data for their plants, the data are usually measured in millimeters per week or millimeters per day. So, if a field of one crop has an evapotranspiration rate of 10 mm per week, it means that the amount of water transferred from the field to the air is the amount of water that would cover the field to a height of 10mm. Imagine the whole field covered with 10 mm of water. That is how much water will be lost to evapotranspiration each week. Of course, the water that the plants use is not taken from the surface of the field, but from the spaces in the soil.

In California, the evapotranspiration of most plants is usually greater than the amount of rain that falls during the growing season. This difference is made up with irrigation water. In the Northeast, evapotranspiration and the ability of the soil to hold water are more in balance with the amount of rainfall crops need. Therefore, few farmers in the Northeast use irrigation to grow crops.

Remember the different soil types you studied and the different amounts of water they were able to hold. If there is more water in the soil than plants need, the plants do not use up the extra water. Plants only take what they need and leave the remaining water in storage. If there is not enough water available, plants will be stressed and might not grow as well as they could. However, there are crops, such as grapes, that farmers deliberately put under water stress during part of the growing season to get larger fruit or other favorable results.

Different plants use different amounts of water as they grow, so farmers need to be aware of how much water their crops will use. The table below shows the evapotranspiration rates for several different crops over the course of a year. Look at these data and answer the analysis questions.

## Analysis Questions

1. On what date does each of the crops begin to require water? When do they stop needing water?

2. How much water do beans need in August?

3. During which month are the water needs for most of the crops the highest?

4. Graph the data for two of the crops and describe the differences you see.

5. If you lived in a place that did not get any rain from January until April, which of these crops would be best to grow? Why?

6. Answer the essential question: *What can you learn from an evapotranspiration graph?*

## Table and Graph

**Evapotranspiration of various crops in Fresno, California**

(Values are in mm of water per month.)

| Crop | January | February | March | April | May | June | July | August | September | October | November | December | Total (mm) |
|------|---------|----------|-------|-------|-----|------|------|--------|-----------|---------|----------|----------|------------|
| artichokes | 20 | 31 | 47 | 93 | 0 | 0 | 55 | 92 | 93 | 63 | 30 | 24 | 548 |
| beans | 0 | 0 | 0 | 0 | 0 | 50 | 171 | 169 | 119 | 0 | 0 | 0 | 509 |
| corn | 0 | 0 | 0 | 33 | 84 | 124 | 147 | 127 | 81 | 41 | 3 | 0 | 640 |
| cotton | 0 | 0 | 0 | 0 | 28 | 68 | 208 | 205 | 162 | 62 | 0 | 0 | 733 |
| grapes | 0 | 0 | 0 | 66 | 114 | 154 | 202 | 148 | 113 | 54 | 0 | 0 | 851 |
| lettuce | 0 | 0 | 8 | 41 | 97 | 155 | 82 | 0 | 0 | 0 | 0 | 0 | 383 |
| peaches | 0 | 0 | 45 | 107 | 138 | 194 | 263 | 194 | 152 | 45 | 0 | 0 | 1138 |
| peppers | 0 | 0 | 58 | 119 | 142 | 179 | 235 | 167 | 0 | 0 | 0 | 0 | 900 |
| rice | 0 | 0 | 0 | 0 | 166 | 208 | 280 | 207 | 156 | 0 | 0 | 0 | 1017 |
| tomatoes | 0 | 0 | 0 | 36 | 72 | 185 | 281 | 174 | 0 | 0 | 0 | 0 | 748 |

**Evapotranspiration for California Crops**

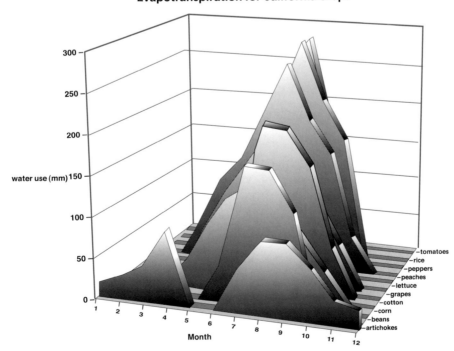

## Lesson 4

# Farm Water Budgets

**?** ***Driving Question:*** *How does soil type affect the types of plants grown on a farm?*

## Overview

In this lesson, you'll use a spreadsheet software program. You'll look at the relationship between rainfall and the water needs of certain plants. The spreadsheet will let you look at different soil types, crops, and locations to see how these factors interact on a farm field. Remember what you learned about available water and wilting point from the soil chapter. Once you have a good idea how water, crops, and rainfall are connected, move on to the next lesson. In the next lesson, you'll see what farmers do when there isn't enough water to grow crops in their fields.

## Important Content

- The time of year when plants in California need the most water is when the least amount is available naturally.

- Evapotranspiration varies by crop type, plant size, and life cycle stage.

# Water, Soil & Crop Relationships on a Farm

 **Essential Question:** *What factors determine how a crop in a particular field will grow?*

## Overview

Have you heard of a household budget? A household budget is a plan for how to spend money. A budget is important to make sure the household does not spend more money than it takes in. Because water is as essential to a farm as money is to a household, farms have water budgets. A farm water budget is used to keep track of the incoming and outgoing water on a farm.

Today, you will look at a simple version of the Farm Water Budget (you will be using a more detailed version later). This tool can help you compare water availability with the water needs of crops. By the end of this lesson, you should know how to use the spreadsheet and understand the relationships among its variables.

Remember that a hectare is the area of a square 100 meters on each side, or about 2.4 acres. You can visualize one hectare as about the size of two football fields.

*(Hint: If you are unsure of the meaning of a word or phrase, click on it to see a picture and a definition.)*

## Background

To be successful, farmers needs to consider many different factors. They must consider the geographical area, including rainfall, temperature, and topography. They must consider the soil type in the fields, which determine the field capacity and the wilting point of the soil. They must also consider the types of crops that will grow well in these conditions. You will study three different farmers, all of whom have 100 hectares of land. Farmer A has a sandy loam soil, he would like to grow corn, and he lives in Texas. Farmer B has a loam soil, would like to grow beans, and lives in Wisconsin. Farmer C has a sand soil, would like to grow rice, and lives in California.

*(Hint: Fill out the Key Elements box to help you find information quickly during the activity.)*

| **Key Elements** | *Farmer A* | *Farmer B* | *Farmer C* |
|---|---|---|---|
| *Field Area* | | | |
| *Soil Type* | | | |
| *Crop Type* | | | |
| *Location* | | | |

# Materials

*Microsoft Excel* installed on a Windows computer

**Farm Water Budget Calculator spreadsheet file**

File name: `Farm Water Budget.xls`

Worksheet Name: `Month`

File type: *Microsoft Excel* spreadsheet.

| ◇ | A | B | C | D | E | F | G | H | I | J | K | L | M |
|---|---|---|---|---|---|---|---|---|---|---|---|---|---|
| 1 | Location: | | | | Soil Type | | | | | | Name: | | |
| 2 | Crop Type | | | | Field Capacity of Soil | | 0 | mm | | | Period: | | |
| 3 | | | | | Wilting Point of Soil | | 0 | mm | | | Date: | | |
| 4 | | | | | Field Area | | | hectares | | | | | |
| 5 | | | | | | | | | | | | | |
| 6 | Stage | Units | First Month | | | | | | | | | | |
| 7 | Precipitation | mm | 0 | | | | | | | | | | |
| 8 | Potential Evapotranspiration | mm | 0 | | | | | | | | | | |
| 9 | Soil Moisture Storage | mm | 0 | | | | | | | | | | |
| 10 | Actual Evapotranspiration | mm | 0 | | | | | | | | | | |
| 11 | Surplus | mm | 0 | | | | | | | | | | |
| 12 | Plant Status | | | | | | | | | | | | |
| 13 | Month | | | | | | | | | | | | |
| 14 | | | | | | | | | | | | | |

**Blank Spreadsheet screen**

# Procedure

1. Follow your teacher's instructions to open the Farm Water Budget Calculator to the Month worksheet. This spreadsheet will accept input from you in the yellow cells only. To begin, make sure that every yellow cell is blank.

2. Enter the Field Area (G4).

3. Enter the soil type for Farmer A in the Soil Type field (G1). Observe what happens to the worksheet. Repeat this process for Farmers B & C.

---

**Stop and Think #1**

Describe what happens to the worksheet when the soil types are entered. How do these numbers relate to one another?

---

4. Delete the information in the Soil Type field.

5. Enter the crop type for Farmer A in the Crop Type field (B2). Notice the changes in the spreadsheet. Repeat for farmers B & C.

6. Delete the information from the Crop Type field.

7. Enter the location of Farmer A in the Location field (B1). Notice the changes in the spreadsheet. Repeat for Farmers B & C.

> **Stop and Think #2**
>
> Why is there a surplus for each farmer?

8. Enter all of the information available for Farmer A.

9. Repeat Steps 7 & 8 for each farmer.

## Analysis Questions

1. What two values in the farm water budget depend on the soil type?

2. In the next lesson, you will be looking at a full year's crop growth. What row could you look at in the spreadsheet to see the growth cycle of this plant?

3. Which farmer's crop will do fairly well in the first month of growth? Why is the outcome different for the other two farmers? Give evidence for this by referring to the values in the spreadsheet. (Hint: The amount of water needed by the plants must be less than or equal to the amount of water available.)

4. Answer the essential question: *What factors determine how a crop in a particular field will grow?*

# Soil Types

 **Essential Question:** *How do different soils affect the water needs of crops?*

## Overview

Different farms, different fields within the farm, and even different parts of the same field may have different soils. Today, you will explore what it means to have different soil types to grow a crop. You will look at how soil type changes the amount of water required to produce a successful crop. You will also study the times of the year when fields have enough water and when they do not have enough water to meet the needs of their crops.

## Materials

 *Microsoft Excel* installed on a Windows computer

 **Farm Water Budget Calculator spreadsheet file**

File name: `Farm Water Budget.xls`

Worksheet Name: `Yearly Budget`

File type: *Microsoft Excel* spreadsheet.

## Procedure

1. Follow your teacher's instructions to open the Yearly Budget worksheet in the Farm Water Budget Calculator. This spreadsheet will accept input from you in the yellow cells only. The difference between this spreadsheet and the previous one is that this spreadsheet shows you the amount of water used on a farm for an entire year instead of just one month. To begin, make sure that every yellow cell is blank.

2. Start by studying a 100 hectare farm in Texas that grows corn and has a sandy loam soil type. Enter the farm's location, field area, crop type, and soil type into the spreadsheet.

**Blank spreadsheet screen**

| | A | B | C | D | E | F | G | H | I | J | K | L | M | N | O |
|---|---|---|---|---|---|---|---|---|---|---|---|---|---|---|---|
| 1 | Location: | | | | | Soil Type | | | | | | | Name: | | |
| 2 | Crop Type | | | | | Field Capacity of Soil | | 0 | mm | | | | Period | | |
| 3 | Growth Period: | | | | | Wilting Point of Soil | | 0 | mm | | | | Date: | | |
| 4 | | | | | | Field Area | | | hectares | | | | | | |

| | A | B | Units | January | February | March | April | May | June | July | August | September | October | November | December | Annual Water Use (mm) |
|---|---|---|---|---|---|---|---|---|---|---|---|---|---|---|---|---|
| 6 | Stage | | Units | | | | | | | | | | | | | |
| 7 | Precipitation | | mm | 0 | 0 | 0 | 0 | 0 | 0 | 0 | 0 | 0 | 0 | 0 | 0 | 0 |
| 8 | Potential Evapotranspiration | | mm | 0 | 0 | 0 | 0 | 0 | 0 | 0 | 0 | 0 | 0 | 0 | 0 | 0 |
| 9 | Soil Moisture Storage | | mm | 0 | 0 | 0 | 0 | 0 | 0 | 0 | 0 | 0 | 0 | 0 | 0 | |
| 10 | Actual Evapotranspiration | | mm | 0 | 0 | 0 | 0 | 0 | 0 | 0 | 0 | 0 | 0 | 0 | 0 | 0 |
| 11 | Surplus | | mm | 0 | 0 | 0 | 0 | 0 | 0 | 0 | 0 | 0 | 0 | 0 | 0 | 0 |
| 12 | Plant Status | | | | | | | | | | | | | | | |
| 13 | Month Status | | | | | | | | | | | | | | | |
| 14 | Year-to-Date Results | | | | | | | | | | | | Crop Yield | | |
| 15 | | | | | | | | | | | | | | | | |

## Stop and Think #1

Describe what happens to the monthly soil moisture storage for all months when these items are entered. *(Hint: Enter items one at a time, observing how the spreadsheet changes with each addition.)*

3. Enter the growth period of corn into the Growth Period box (B3). You can determine the growth period by looking at the months where the plant is using water through evapotranspiration. If the plant is using water, it is alive. Enter growth period as a range of months (for example, "Jan-June").

4. Change the soil type to clay.

## Stop and Think #2

What happens to the crop in clay soil as compared with the same crop in sandy loam soil? Why?

5. Change the location to California. Notice changes in the spreadsheet.

6. Change the location to Wisconsin. Again, notice the changes.

## Stop and Think #3

How does the geographic location affect the crop? Why does this occur?

7. Compare two different farmers. Both are going to grow artichokes in sand soil. The difference between them is that one lives in Wisconsin and the other lives in Texas. What will the outcomes be for each?

> **Stop and Think #4**
>
> What is the difference in the crop yields between the two farms? Why?

8. Answer Analysis Question 1 by experimenting with the different combinations of soil types and geographic locations.

## Analysis Questions

1. If corn is the crop that you are going to grow, which combination of soil and geographic location provides the best environment for your crop? Why?

2. What could a farmer do to prevent corn plants from wilting?

3. Answer the essential question: *How do different soils affect the water needs of crops?*

# Crop Types

**Essential Question:** *What factors should farmers take into account when they are planning what crops to plant?*

## Overview

You will again explore farm issues by working with the Farm Water Budget spreadsheet. You have explored having different types of soils on farms in the previous lesson. In this activity, you will explore how different crops affect the water balance on a farm. By understanding the effects of soil and crop type, you will have a clear picture of all of the natural interactions that affect crop production on a farm.

## Background

Imagine Farmer Bob wants to purchase some additional land so he can grow more crops. There are two 80-hectare pieces of land that have come up for sale next to his Wisconsin farm. The two fields have different soil types. Considering that different soils affect crop production, he needs to figure out what type of crop could successfully grow on either of these fields. The soil type in Field A is silt loam and the soil type on Field B is sand. By understanding how these soil types will affect his intended crop, Farmer Bob can make a better decision about his purchase.

| Key Elements | Field A | Field B |
|---|---|---|
| Location | | |
| Soil Type | | |

## Materials

 *Microsoft Excel* installed on a Windows computer

 **Farm Water Budget Calculator spreadsheet file**

File name: `Farm Water Budget.xls`

Worksheet Name: `Yearly Budget`

File type: *Microsoft Excel* spreadsheet.

**Blank spreadsheet screen**

| | A | B | C | D | E | F | G | H | I | J | K | L | M | N | O |
|---|---|---|---|---|---|---|---|---|---|---|---|---|---|---|---|
| 1 | Location: | | | | | Soil Type | | | | | | | Name: | | |
| 2 | Crop Type | | | | | Field Capacity of Soil | | 0 | mm | | | | Period | | |
| 3 | Growth Period: | | | | | Wilting Point of Soil | | 0 | mm | | | | Date: | | |
| 4 | | | | | | Field Area | | | hectares | | | | | | |
| 5 | | | | | | | | | | | | | | | |
| 6 | **Stage** | **Units** | January | February | March | April | May | June | July | August | September | October | November | December | Annual Water Use (mm) |
| 7 | Precipitation | mm | 0 | 0 | 0 | 0 | 0 | 0 | 0 | 0 | 0 | 0 | 0 | 0 | 0 |
| 8 | Potential Evapotranspiration | mm | 0 | 0 | 0 | 0 | 0 | 0 | 0 | 0 | 0 | 0 | 0 | 0 | 0 |
| 9 | Soil Moisture Storage | mm | 0 | 0 | 0 | 0 | 0 | 0 | 0 | 0 | 0 | 0 | 0 | 0 | |
| 10 | Actual Evapotranspiration | mm | 0 | 0 | 0 | 0 | 0 | 0 | 0 | 0 | 0 | 0 | 0 | 0 | 0 |
| 11 | Surplus | mm | 0 | 0 | 0 | 0 | 0 | 0 | 0 | 0 | 0 | 0 | 0 | 0 | 0 |
| 12 | **Plant Status** | | | | | | | | | | | | | | |
| 13 | **Month Status** | | | | | | | | | | | | | | |
| 14 | **Year-to-Date Results** | | | | | | | | | | Crop Yield | | | | |
| 15 | | | | | | | | | | | | | | | |

# Procedure

1. Open the Farm Water Budget Spreadsheet to the Yearly Worksheet. Test the different available crop types for Field A. *(Hint: The crops that are valid within the spreadsheet are corn, beans, tomatoes, artichokes, lettuce, peppers or rice.)*

2. Test the different available crop types for Field B.

# Analysis Questions

1. Which field should Farmer Bob purchase? Why?

2. If Farmer Bob decides to grow peppers on Field A, in which months does the actual evapotranspiration rate differ from the potential evapotranspiration? Why do you think this is? What effect does this have on the corn plants?

3. If he decides to grow beans, in which months is the risk of flooding the greatest? Explain your reasoning. What could this do to the crop?

4. If Field B was the only plot for sale and Farmer Bob needed to grow corn as his crop, what could he do to ensure the success of this crop on this plot of land?

5. Answer the essential question: *What factors should farmers take into account when they are planning what crops to plant?*

# Lesson 5
# Irrigation

 **Driving Question:** *What type of irrigation is most effective at meeting water needs of plants?*

## Overview

In some areas of the U.S., rainfall is usually sufficient for crop growth. For example, in the Northeast, very few farmers rely on irrigation to water their crops. Therefore, in this region, farmers plant crops that thrive on the amount of rainfall the region normally gets.

You have seen that in some areas of the country, rainfall does not always provide enough water to keep crops alive. This is a problem many farmers face, especially in California. In fact, irrigation for agriculture uses most of the water supply in the Fresno, California area. Irrigation in California is critical for plant growth because the average rainfall per year is less than the rate of evapotranspiration. In other areas of the country, irrigation is used only in the summer to supplement rainfall. In the Midwest, groundwater is used to supplement rainwater and irrigate crops. The use of irrigation has increased the diversity and amount of produce in our stores, but it has also caused controversy. In this lesson, you will explore irrigation through a lab activity and work with a computer spreadsheet. You will also look at several farms that changed their irrigation practices to conserve water.

## Important Content

- The three main classes of irrigation systems used in the United States are gravity, sprinkler, and micro-irrigation.

- Because efficiency rates differ, the choice of irrigation system can make a big difference in the amount of water used on a farm.

# Water for Plants

 *Essential Question:* How can we get irrigation water to plants?

## Overview

In the last lesson, you saw that rainfall does not always supply enough water for plants. When that happens, farmers must irrigate, or add water to their fields so crops can grow. Today, you will use your knowledge of soil and plants to design an irrigation system for a farm. The irrigation system should get water to all of the plants in the field and should minimize the amount of water wasted.

## Materials

Begin with the following, but feel free to ask your teacher for additional materials.
- tray of soil to represent the farm (it should have holes at one end for drainage)
- bendable drinking straws for water delivery
- paper clips and clay for connecting straws to each other

## Safety

Follow standard safety rules and school safety rules for laboratory activities.

## Procedure

Do the following for each sponge.

1. Put a book under one end of your soil tray so water will run down in one direction.

2. Using your supplies, design a way to get water to the plants in the farm. Try to:

   a. deliver equal amounts of water to all areas of the field

   b. minimize runoff (water pooling at the edge of the field instead of in the soil)

## Analysis Questions

1. Draw a picture and write a paragraph to describe your irrigation system.

2. How would you adjust your irrigation system for different types of soil? (For example, compare a sand soil system to a clay soil system.)

3. How would you design your system differently if you knew your plants were spaced widely apart?

4. How would you design your system differently if you knew there was very little space between the plants growing on your farm?

5. Answer the essential question: *How can we get irrigation water to plants?*

# Irrigation Systems

 **Essential Question:** *What are the costs and benefits of each type of irrigation?*

## Overview

Today, you will read about the different types of irrigation systems a farmer can use. This information will be helpful in upcoming lessons where you will use the Farm Water Budget spreadsheet and irrigate your farms.

## Irrigation Systems

Irrigation is the practice of transporting water to crops. Irrigation has been around for at least 7,000 years, since the beginnings of agriculture. The ancient Egyptians irrigated their fields with water from the Nile River. Grain seeds were placed in the mud left after the Nile's floodwaters receded, giving the seeds the moisture they needed to sprout. In some places, channels were dug to allow water to flow from the Nile to the fields. These channels were opened when the farmers knew their plants needed water.

Irrigation technology has come a long way in 7,000 years, but its goals are still the same. Today, farmers analyze the evapotranspiration of their crops as a way to manage their irrigation needs. Irrigation is used to achieve maximum crop yields, so it must meet the crop's potential evapotranspiration value.

When farmers decide which systems to use for their fields, there are a number of factors they need to consider. The first factor is efficiency. Some systems are more efficient than others in certain situations. Farmers need to know which system best meets their needs and can increase crop yields without using excess water. Another factor farmers have to consider is cost. Farmers must pay for irrigation systems that tap into water that comes from rivers or for pumping water from the ground. Water is becoming scarcer in many agricultural regions in the U.S. and around the world. That means farmers might want to look for the most cost-efficient and environmentally sound ways of delivering water to their crops.

### Irrigation Methods

These are the three basic ways to irrigate crops:

*Surface or gravity irrigation*

One form of irrigation is called surface irrigation. As its name suggests, surface irrigation directs water over the surface of the farm field to the crops. The water travels along channels dug in the soil between rows of plants. A variation of surface irrigation is gravity irrigation. Gravity irrigation allows water to flow through a channel from an uphill source to a crop field downhill. In both cases, gates are often placed in the channels to control water flow. Gravity irrigation has the advantage of not requiring energy to pump the water because gravity provides

the energy. Some surface irrigation requires an energy source to move the water from the lake or river through the channel to the field.

Because surface and gravity irrigation involve water traveling on top of the surface, some of the water evaporates before it reaches the plants or sinks into the soil. However, because it is relatively simple and doesn't require a lot of energy, surface irrigation is a widely used irrigation method.

*Sprinklers*

Another system widely used in the U.S. is sprinkler irrigation. Sprinklers are mechanical devices that spray water over crops to simulate rain. Some systems are permanently installed and others are portable.

One of the most commonly used sprinkler systems is center-pivot irrigation. If you have flown on a plane, you may have seen the large circles of green on some farm fields far below. The circles are the areas covered by center-pivot sprinklers. Center-pivot irrigation involves pumping water up into a central shaft in the system. When the system is turned on, the water moves continually through the central shaft to huge sprayer arms that extend many meters on either side. Each sprayer arm has holes from which the water flows. The entire sprinkler turns, or pivots, around the central shaft, watering the crops as it spins.

Some of the factors farmers need to consider with sprinkler irrigation systems are their cost and efficiency. In addition to buying the machinery, farmers have the cost of the electricity needed to pump water into the sprinkler and to generate high pressure to shoot the water out of the sprinklers. Depending on weather and other factors, up to 50% of the water sprayed from these systems is lost to evaporation before it reaches the ground. Much of the water evaporates on plant leaves or on the soil surface before it reaches plant roots.

*Micro-irrigation*

Micro-irrigation involves adding water directly to plant roots as they need it. There are a number of different kinds of micro-irrigation systems. One is a spray or micro-sprinkler system. This is different from other sprinkler systems in that water is sprayed right near the base of the plants. This method can wet an area 8 to 30 feet in diameter.

Another form of micro-irrigation is drip irrigation. Drip irrigation delivers a measured amount of water through an emitter, usually a piece of flexible tubing with holes, which is located on the soil near each plant. A typical drip emitter will release about one gallon of water per hour and wet only a small volume of soil near plant roots. Because water is delivered from tubes directly on the soil, most of the water seeps into the soil, where plant roots can reach it. In some types of drip irrigation, the tubing is buried under the soil. This is called subsurface drip micro-irrigation. Water is delivered through underground drip lines, irrigating the root systems of plants directly. The water does not evaporate because it is not exposed to the air. All of the water is delivered directly to the sub-soil region around plant roots. This kind of system is especially efficient for a permanent crop, such as trees and grapevines, where the roots are in the same place from season to season.

## Comparing Irrigation Techniques

Which of these irrigation techniques is best? There are advantages and disadvantages to each one, and each one is best for different locations, crops, and conditions.

Many people believe surface or gravity irrigation is less efficient than sprinkler or drip irrigation since water evaporates during transfer. However, surface irrigation uses less energy to transport (or pump) water than sprinkler irrigation. It also may be the most practical and efficient where there are uniform soils and slopes and crops are grown on large fields.

In some cases, surface or gravity irrigation is the preferred choice. Field crops such as alfalfa or cereal grains are usually irrigated this way, along field borders. Rice is usually irrigated by the surface or gravity method. Farmers use these irrigation methods because sprinklers are too expensive for crops with lower market value. An added benefit to some surface or gravity irrigation systems is that excess water can seep into the soil, feeding underground aquifers.

Irrigation systems such as drip or micro-sprinkler apply water evenly and efficiently. They are the most practical where fields do not slope or where permanent crops are being grown. A recent study shows that 20% of all irrigated agriculture in California uses micro-irrigation. Because micro-irrigation is more useful for permanent crops, 65% of farms growing subtropical fruits, such as citrus use micro-irrigation systems. Permanent drip or sprinkler systems work well with crops grown in orchards or vineyards, but not with crops that require complete annual replanting, such as tomatoes or broccoli.

Drip irrigation has another advantage over the other systems. It can supply small, carefully controlled quantities of fertilizer to the plants, as they need it. The fertilizer is simply added to the water that flows through the tubing. Other beneficial chemicals can also be delivered in small quantities in this way. Studies have shown that plants given small quantities of fertilizer frequently with drip irrigation systems produce better crops. Insect damage to plants is also reduced because leaf surfaces are drier and attract fewer insects.

Drip irrigation has its drawbacks, however. Tubing can clog and have to be cleaned or replaced, adding expense of the system. Like other forms of irrigation, drip irrigation may also lead to salinization (increased salt content) of the soil, which can be harmful for plants.

There is also another potential drawback to micro-irrigation systems. While these systems are becoming much more common as the technology improves, installing these systems is expensive. Farmers who have invested in sprinkler irrigators may not want to spend more money on a new micro-irrigation system.

When farmers have decided which irrigation system is best for them, they have a variety of tools available to help them make their irrigation methods as efficient as possible. Computer software programs can perform diagnostic tests and aid irrigation management. These programs analyze irrigation patterns and simulate irrigation throughout the year. They then provide an annual summary and give tips for improvement. Farmers can also use mobile irrigation management labs. These labs are locally funded and bring irrigation science directly to the farm.

They are equipped with the latest in technology and provide farmers with irrigation evaluations and a summary of water and dollar savings. Timing of irrigation is crucial no matter what method is used. Effective scheduling reduces the total amount of water applied during a season and improves water use efficiency.

According to the California Department of Water Resources, efficient irrigation can lead to:

- increased crop yield
- improved quality of yield
- reduced use and conservation of water, energy, and money
- reduction in the costs of labor, pesticides, and fertilizers
- prevention of contaminated surface water and groundwater

## Analysis Questions

1. What are the three major types of irrigation systems?

2. What are two ways in which sprinkler irrigation wastes water?

3. How can modern technology aid farmers in irrigating their fields efficiently?

4. Answer the essential question: *What are the advantages and disadvantages of different types of irrigation?*

# Precipitation and Irrigation

***Essential Question:*** *How can farmers determine when it is appropriate to irrigate their fields?*

## Overview

In the last reading, Irrigation Systems, you read that irrigation can be expensive and time-consuming. Because of this, farmers only want to irrigate their crops when it is necessary. You have seen that one way farmers can achieve this is by carefully planning and scheduling when to irrigate. Efficient scheduling involves attention to many details. One thing the farmer needs to know is the available water in the soil and how much water each crop needs. Available water is the amount of water a plant can get out of the soil. As you may remember from the Sponges experiment in the previous chapter, if the amount of water in the soil is below the wilting point, there is no water available for plants. When this is the case, the farmer needs to add water. If the amount of water goes above the field capacity, the soil cannot hold any more water. The excess water will be lost to runoff or will be lost as it seeps below the plants' roots.

There are also a number of other factors farmers need to be aware of in order to irrigate their fields effectively. For instance, farmers need to pay attention to weather conditions. Farmers need to know how much precipitation (rain) is expected and how much precipitation has already fallen throughout the year. That way they can figure out how much more water their crops need. However, farmers can only calculate the extra water their crops need if they know specific information about the crops in their field. They need to know the stage of the crops' development, how much water it needs at each stage, and when it can be harvested. This kind of information is contained in the evapotranspiration values available from a government agency called the agricultural extension. Besides being experts on their crops, farmers also need to know about special conditions in the fields that might affect crop growth and water usage. The farmer then has to choose a minimum water budget balance to maintain the field above the wilting point. Being able to make this kind of informed decision is important, especially in farming communities like those in Fresno, where water resources are being depleted.

In this lesson, you will examine a graph of California precipitation data to explore how farmers can determine their irrigation needs.

## Procedure

The graph on the following page shows the average monthly precipitation in Fresno, CA. It also shows two special years: 1969, a very wet year and 1977, a very dry year. Use the graph to answer the Analysis Questions.

## Analysis Questions

1. Which months tend to have the most precipitation? Which have the least?

2. In what months will farmers in the Fresno area need to irrigate the most? When will they irrigate the least?

3. Answer the essential question: *How can farmers determine when it is appropriate to irrigate their fields?*

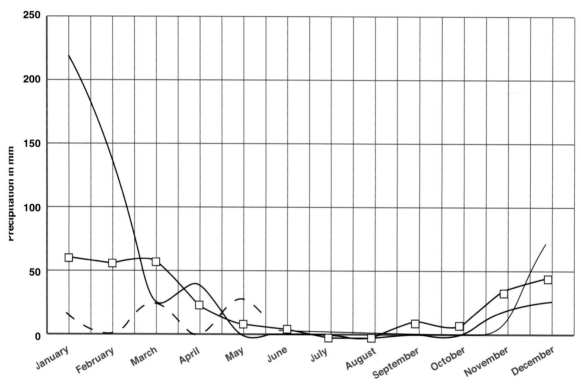

**Precipitation in Fresno**

# Irrigation Efficiency

 *Essential Question: Why is it important to have an efficient irrigation system?*

## Overview

In this activity, you will work with the Farm Water Budget spreadsheet again. By the end of this lesson, you will better understand how to irrigate your field effectively.

## Background

Farmers always want to make sure their crops get enough water. That is why they use irrigation systems to get water to their crops. But what happens when an irrigation system is inefficient? Inefficient irrigation is using too much water. The excess water may evaporate from the soil, run off the field to a lake or stream, or seep deep into the ground. Using too much water can be costly for farmers. The water costs farmers money, as does the transportation of the water to the plants. Not only can using too much water be a waste of money, but it can also harm the plants. Too much water in the soil can prevent plant roots from taking up oxygen or other important nutrients from the soil. Farmers try to minimize these losses, but they cannot eliminate them. Farmers want to achieve the ideal water content in the soil. When they do, their irrigation system will be more effective, and their plants will be healthier.

Different crops require different amounts of water to mature. Most crops require 900 mm or more of usable water per year. To get that much water to plant roots, farmers could apply this amount of water to the fields. However, they have to take into consideration yearly rainfall and the amount of irrigation water lost to seepage, evaporation, and runoff.

Not all irrigation systems lose the same amount of water to seepage, evaporation and runoff, though. Different types of irrigation have different efficiencies. That means that more water is lost with some systems than with others and that some can do a better job of getting water to plants than others. These varying efficiencies are caused by evaporation or by irrigating parts of the field that are not near roots. The approximate efficiencies of irrigation systems are listed in the table below. These numbers represent the percentage of water applied to a field that is usable by plants.

**Table: Irrigation Efficiencies**

| Type of Irrigation | Approximate Efficiency |
|---|---|
| Border-Strip (gravity) | 75% |
| Basin (gravity) | 75% |
| Furrow (gravity) | 75% |
| Sprinkler | 80% |
| Drip (micro-irrigation) | 94% |
| Spray/micro-sprinkler irrigation | 94% |
| Subsurface drip (row crops) | 96% |
| Subsurface drip (permanent crops) | 99% |

Any water that evaporates before it soaks into the soil decreases efficiency. Water applied to areas where no plants are growing also decreases efficiency.

Here are two assumptions being used in the Farm Water Budget spreadsheet:

1. All the rain came at the beginning of the month and the plants used the water after that.

2. Plants could often still use water in the soil even if it exceeded field capacity.

In reality, rain can come anytime in the month. Plants may need water before the rain comes. Likewise, some of the excess rainwater will run off the surface of the field, not giving the plants a chance to use it. Farmers must plan for these possibilities when they irrigate. Irrigation is only part science because needs cannot always be predicted exactly. Farmers use tools, like water budgets, as guidelines to help them judge when they should think about irrigating. They also must consider factors that are difficult to measure like weather, differences in individual soils, and lessons they have learned from past experiences.

## Materials

*Microsoft Excel* installed on a Windows computer

**Farm Water Budget spreadsheet file**

File name: Farm Water Budget.xls

Worksheet Name: Irrigation

File type: *Microsoft Excel* spreadsheet.

### Blank worksheet

| | A | B | C | D | E | F | G | H | I | J | K | L | M | N | O |
|---|---|---|---|---|---|---|---|---|---|---|---|---|---|---|---|
| 1 | Location: | | | | | Soil Type | | | | | | | Name: | | |
| 2 | Crop Type | | | | | Field Capacity | | 0 | mm | | | | Period: | | |
| 3 | Growth Period: | | | | | Wilting Point of Soil | | 0 | mm | | | | Date: | | |
| 4 | Irrigation Efficiency | | | | | Field Area | | | hectares | | | | | | |
| 5 | | | | | | | | | | | | | | | |
| 6 | Stage | Units | January | February | March | April | May | June | July | August | September | October | November | December | Annual Water Use (mm) |
| 7 | Precipitation | mm | 0 | 0 | 0 | 0 | 0 | 0 | 0 | 0 | 0 | 0 | 0 | 0 | 0 |
| 8 | Irrigation | mm | | | | | | | | | | | | | 0 |
| 9 | Actual Irrigation | mm | 0 | 0 | 0 | 0 | 0 | 0 | 0 | 0 | 0 | 0 | 0 | 0 | 0 |
| 10 | Potential Evapotranspiration | mm | 0 | 0 | 0 | 0 | 0 | 0 | 0 | 0 | 0 | 0 | 0 | 0 | 0 |
| 11 | Soil Moisture Storage | mm | 0 | 0 | 0 | 0 | 0 | 0 | 0 | 0 | 0 | 0 | 0 | 0 | |
| 12 | Actual Evapotranspiration | mm | 0 | 0 | 0 | 0 | 0 | 0 | 0 | 0 | 0 | 0 | 0 | 0 | 0 |
| 13 | Surplus | mm | 0 | 0 | 0 | 0 | 0 | 0 | 0 | 0 | 0 | 0 | 0 | 0 | 0 |
| 14 | Plant Status | | | | | | | | | | | | | | |
| 15 | Month Status | | | | | | | | | | | | | | |
| 16 | Irrigation Status | | | | | | | | | | | | | | |
| 17 | Year-to-Date Results | | | | | | | | | | Crop Yield | | Irrigation YTD | | |
| 18 | | | | | | | | | | | | | | | |

## Procedure

1. Open the Farm Water Budget spreadsheet to the Irrigation page.

2. Create a water budget for a 100-hectare farm in California that grows tomatoes. Assume sandy loam conditions.

3. Place the irrigation efficiency at 100%.

4. Irrigate your field by entering the amount of irrigation required for each month into the Irrigation row. Adjust the irrigation numbers for your field so that the irrigation status and plant status rows indicate "OK." (There should be no stress on the plants.)

5. Record the total annual amount of water used for irrigation.

6. Repeat Steps 1-4 with at least three other types of irrigation. Remember that each irrigation type has a different percent efficiency. Record your results in a chart.

> **Stop and Think**
>
> What happens to your irrigation results when you change the irrigation type? Why?

## Analysis Questions

1. What would happen if the local county limited farms to 175 mm of water per month for irrigation? Could you still grow tomatoes?

2. Answer the essential question: *Why is it important to have an efficient irrigation system?*

# Irrigation Case Studies

 **Essential Question:** *When is it cost-effective to change irrigation systems?*

## Overview

On the following pages, there are three case studies of farms that upgraded their irrigation systems. Your task is to evaluate their results.

## Background

Changing the irrigation system on a farm can have many consequences. The amount of water used could change because of less evaporation on the surface of the soil. The amount of energy used could change if the new irrigation system requires more pumping or requires higher water pressure. Crop yield could change because of the increase or decrease in available water near the roots.

## Procedure

Read each of the case studies and answer the Analysis Questions below.

## Analysis Questions

The first four questions should be answered for each case study.

1. What was the approximate water savings realized by the new technology?

2. What was the approximate amount of yield change realized by the new technology?

3. Using the average crop price, calculate the income the farm generated before and after the irrigation system was installed.

4. Suppose all of the extra money made by each farm is used to repay the loan on the new irrigation system. How long will it take each farm to repay the loan?

5. In Case Study 1, water use in 1995 was much higher than in 1992. Does this mean that installing the new irrigation system was a failure? Why or why not? *(Hint: think about how many tons of peppers were grown each year.)*

6. Answer the essential question: *When is it cost-effective to change irrigation systems?*

## Case Study 1: Smith Farms

Smith Farms is a 16-hectare site located in Northern California. It installed a new, buried row, crop drip irrigation system in 1993 to improve the yield on pepper crops. The new system was paid for with a loan of $42,700. The installation of the system provided significant improvements in the amount of water use, energy required, and yield increases, especially in the first (1993) and the third (1995) year of operation.

In the second year of the project (1994), the yield did not increase.

Note: MBTU stands for one million British Thermal Units (BTU). This is a common way to measure energy use.

### Project Summary

|  |  |
|---|---|
| **Loan** | $42,700 |
| **Crop** | bell peppers (green) |
| **Average Sales Price** | $295 per ton |
| **Size of field** | 16 hectares |
| **Technology Evaluated** | drip irrigation, buried-row crop drip compared to sprinkler/surface irrigation |

## Resources and Results

| Year | Yield Tons/hectare | Energy Use MBTUs/hectare | Water Use mm |
|---|---|---|---|
| 1992[1] | 44 | 46 | 820 |
| 1993 | 58 | 54 | 730 |
| 1994 | 44 | 54 | 730 |
| 1995 | 81 | 62 | 950 |

[1] Before installation of new irrigation

## Case Study 2: Castle Ranch

The site is located east of Oxnard, California. The field is a 20-hectare project supplied with a new, buried-row, crop drip irrigation system. The grower formerly irrigated with sprinklers only. The primary crop was jalapeño peppers.

Project Location: East of Oxnard

### *Project Summary*

| | |
|---|---|
| **Loan** | $50,000 |
| **Crop** | jalapeño peppers |
| **Average Sales Price** | $295 per ton |
| **Size of Field** | 20 hectares |
| **Technology Evaluated** | drip irrigation, buried-row crop drip compared to sprinkler/surface irrigation |

### *Resources and Results*

| Year | Yield Tons/hectare | Energy Use MBTUs/hectare | Water Use mm |
|---|---|---|---|
| 1993[2] | 50 | 5 | 710 |
| 1994 | 75 | 55 | 550 |
| 1995 | 55 | 5 | 600 |

[2] Before installation of new irrigation

## Case Study 3: Moore Farms

Moore Farms grows several crops in the southern San Joaquin Valley, including pistachios, almonds, apples, and watermelons. The farm received a loan for the installation of a buried drip system in an established pistachio orchard near Delano, California.

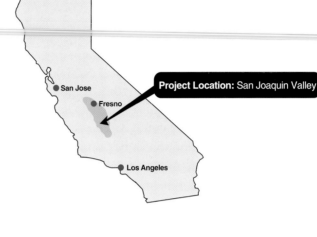

Project Location: San Joaquin Valley

### Project Summary

**Loan** $150,000

**Crop** pistachios

**Average Sales Price** $2000 per ton

**Size of Field** 71 hectares

**Technology Evaluated** drip irrigation, buried drip on permanent trees compared to surface irrigation

### Resources and Results

| Year | Yield Tons/hectare | Energy Use MBTUs/hectare | Water Use mm |
|------|------|------|------|
| 1993[3] | 2.3 | 17 | 1400 |
| 1994 | 4.5 | 9.4 | 1000 |
| 1995 | 4.0 | 9.4 | 1000 |

[3] Before installation of new irrigation

## Lesson 6

# Farming in Fresno

***Driving Question:*** *What factors affect the efficiency of producing the best possible crop yield on a farm?*

## Overview

In this lesson, you will use what you have learned to help a farmer increase his yield. You will use precision farming, a method that relies on technology and careful planning to deliver the exact amount of water and fertilizer needed by plants in the field. In the last lesson, you learned about efficient irrigation, which is an important part of precision farming. WorldWatcher software will provide data about the farmer's field as you choose between three options to help the farm become more productive. You will also use the Environmental Decision Making Process to help you in this task.

## Important Content

*   New technologies and farming methods can increase efficiency, increase profits, and reduce pollution and waste on farms.

*   Precision farming is a combination of efficient irrigation with careful fertilizer and pesticide application.

*   Precision farming uses technology to create detailed pictures of what is happening in different parts of a farmer's field.

# Farmer John

***Essential Question:*** *What are your constraints and considerations for increasing the yield of Farmer John's field?*

## Overview

You have already learned a great deal about how soil affects plant growth. You have also learned how farmers use this knowledge to develop the crops that feed the nation and the world. Now you will have a chance to put this information together in an activity that deals with the exciting new technology of precision farming.

You will use the Environmental Decision Making Process to complete this task, beginning by defining your constraints and considerations. As you know, constraints describe the limitations you are working under. They may be either physical limitations or limitations that come from your personal values. Some of the many factors that can constrain your decision are time, money, laws, or the environmental impact you are willing to tolerate. Constraints are absolute limitations. They cannot be violated in a solution. Considerations are preferences that may or may not be possible. Decision makers try to achieve the most important considerations, keeping in mind their constraints as they consider all the available options.

### Setting the Stage

You work for a company that earns its money by providing advice and analysis to farmers about geographic information systems, soil, and agriculture. You received the letter on the following page.

## Analysis Questions

1. What is Farmer John's ultimate goal for this decision?

2. What do you think he would consider a successful outcome?

3. Answer the essential question: *What are your constraints and considerations for increasing the yield of Farmer John's field?*

Dear Scientists:

My family has farmed our land near Fresno, California for generations. We have always worked hard and earned a fair price for our crop, growing corn and sunflowers. I recently started using precision farming techniques to collect data. I'm hoping that with your data-analysis expertise, you can analyze the data for one of my poorly performing corn fields and make a recommendation about what I might do to improve the yield in that field.

I've known for a while that Field 19 does not have as high a yield as it should, but I have never understood why. When I walk around the field, the corn looks healthy. Nevertheless, the yield for the field is lower than that in the other fields.

I want to increase my yield in this field, but water is scarce. It is also getting more expensive here in California's Central Valley, so I need to be careful about my water use.

To help you with your analysis, I'm sending you WorldWatcher data, showing the field capacity of the soil and the corn yield for last year. The yield is a measurement of the weight of the corn that we've harvested in a particular area of the field. Last year, we used furrow irrigation, with "double-ridge" furrows spaced 1.5 meters apart. This meant that we had two rows of corn plants together on the top of the ridge with a furrow on either side. It looked like this.

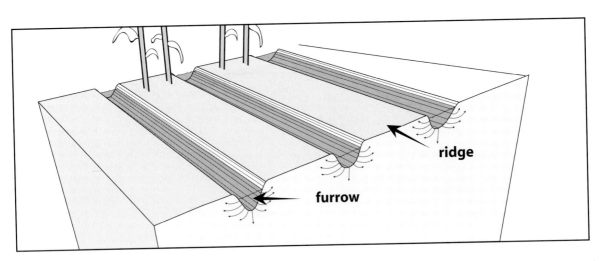

I need to decide what to do next year, and I have several options:

1. I could install a drip irrigation system. This will cost me $99,000 to install, but I've heard that this will increase my yield with less water use.

2. I could switch to single-ridge furrows with 0.75 meter spacing and use 20% more water that I did last year. This would get more water near the roots of the plants that need it most. This would only cost me the price of the additional water. Single ridge furrows would look like this:

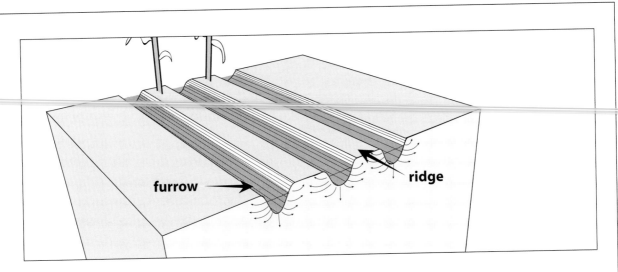

3. I could add more organic material to the low-yield soils in my field. This would improve the soil, increasing field capacity by 15 mm. This will cost me $3000 in labor costs to apply the organic material.

I could also do a combination of these options.

Please let me know how each of these options would affect my yield and water use and which option you think would be best for my farm.

Thank you,

*Farmer John*

Farmer John

# Precision Farming

*Essential Question: What is precision farming and how might it affect agriculture in the coming years?*

## Overview

Precision farming involves using advanced technology to customize crop-growing practices. The technology helps farmers collect accurate data about crop yield and field conditions. These data can then be analyzed so farmers can make informed decisions about growing conditions. Read the following article about precision farming. Then answer the Analysis Questions below.

## An Overview of Precision Farming

Farmers are always looking for ways to increase production, reduce costs, and increase their profits. One way to achieve these goals is through the use of new technologies. Today, large farming corporations have the money to invest in precision farming technology. According to the U.S. Department of Agriculture (USDA), even small- and medium-scale farmers now use computers. Their computers make them potential candidates for precision farming, too.

Precision farming uses advances in electronics for the benefit of agriculture. Farmers can add data collection devices to their farm equipment to gather data with Global Positioning Systems (GPS). Then, the data can be examined with Geographic Information Systems (GIS) to analyze field and crop conditions. For example, farmers can look at the composition of the soil and the terrain throughout their land. This kind of information enables farmers to adjust their practices to match the variation within a field. Being aware of these variations can help a farmer decide what type of crop might grow best in each area. It can also help farmers decide if they need to make changes to their soil or growing practices.

The traditional approach to farming was to treat a whole field in the same way. But precision farming gives farmers the knowledge to adjust their methods the meet the needs of each small section of a field.

Precision farming helps farmers improve their efficiency by matching inputs – such as water, fertilizer, and pesticides – with soil types, climate, and terrain. For instance, the farmer might notice that some sections of the soil are more nutrient-rich than others. With that knowledge, the farmer can add fertilizers just in the areas that need it. Similarly, data might show that some areas of the field are not receiving sufficient water. Without this data, the farmer might have chosen to water the entire field, but with the data, the farmer can selectively water the areas that need it the most. That is why it is called precision farming: the GIS data gives the farmer information which can be used to make very precise decisions about how to best manage every section of a field. Having this kind of information can mean having the ability to grow larger, healthier, more abundant crops with less water.

Having access to this kind of information has changed farming. Precision farming allows farmers to monitor their fields on a small scale. However, that does not ensure that farmers will be able to act on the data at such a small scale. Precision farming provides farmers with data, but they still have to interpret it into useful information that will increase efficiency and yields. In other words, just having the data is not enough. A farmer might be able to see that parts of the farmer's fields have sandy loam soil and other parts have loam soil, but what does that mean? Should the farmer change the crop type to better match the soil variations? Does the farmer have the resources to plant different crops to match the soil variations? Is it economical to vary crop growth on a small scale? While technology can provide useful data, it cannot answer these types of questions. The farmer still has to have the knowledge, resources, and abilities to make decisions based on what the data shows. It might not be possible to respond to variations in the soil and terrain on such a precise level, and the farmer has to know what the data means in order to act on it.

## Analysis Questions

1. How are new technologies being applied to farming?

2. What are the issues of scale in the use of precision farming? Why is this an important issue for farmers?

3. Answer the essential question: *What is precision farming and how might it affect agriculture in the coming years?*

# 1997 Yield Analysis

 ***Essential Question:*** *What was the yield pattern in Farmer John's field in 1997?*

## Overview

To evaluate Farmer John's proposals, you first need to understand what happened in his field in 1997. This lesson will help you explain the yield in his field.

## Materials

 **WorldWatcher** *geographic visualization software*

 • *Farmer John's Corn Yield, 1997*

File name: `yield1997.wwf`

 • *Farmer John's Field Capacity Data*

File name: `FieldCapacity1997.wwf`

## Procedure

1. Open WorldWatcher according to your teacher's instructions. Open the data set: Yield 1997. The number in each cell of this data set shows the number of bushels of corn that were harvested in that cell. A bushel is equal to .35 cubic meters (m3) or 2,150 cubic inches. That's about the size of a small suitcase. Each cell in this data set is about 3.5 meters across going East-West direction and 4 meters across going North-South. *Record your general observations about the yield pattern in this field.*

2. Do a "Select by value" for values greater than 0. This will select all the cells that are in the actual field. At the top of the window, it will tell you the total yield (sum value) for the selection. *Record the total yield for the field. Make sure to include the units (bushels) for this yield number. Also, record the total area of the field. The units for the area are square meters (m2).*

3. Create a histogram of the selection. The histogram window will display the mean (average) yield per cell. *Record the mean yield per cell. Make sure to include the units (bushels) for this yield number.*

4. As a general rule, farmers consider the "break even" point for corn to be .7 bushels per cell. This means that if they harvest more than .7 bushels in a cell, they make money on that cell. If they harvest less, then they lose money on that cell. *Overall, is the farmer making money on this field?*

5. Make a selection that shows the cells that are losing money. *Describe where the money-losing cells occur in the field. Using the total areas of the field and your selection, calculate and record the percentage of the field that is losing money.*

6. Open the data set: Field Capacity 1997. Compare the 1997 yield and field capacity data sets. *Record the average field capacity for the whole field, the average field capacity for the parts of the field that are losing money, and the average field capacity for the parts of the field that are making money.*

> **Stop and Think**
>
> Look back in your notes on field capacity and soil types. Which kinds of soils have lower field capacity?

## Analysis Questions

1. Which sections of Farmer John's field appear to be having problems in 1997? What do you think is causing those problems?

2. Answer the essential question: *What was the yield pattern in Farmer John's field in 1997?*

# 1997 Analyzing Irrigation Needs

**?** *Essential Question:* How much water did Farmer John need to apply to his field in 1997?

## Overview

Before you can make a recommendation to Farmer John, you need to understand how much water he used in 1997. In this activity, you will calculate the minimum amount of water that his field would have required. You will use the spreadsheet you used in Lesson 5: *Irrigation Efficiency*.

## Background

| January | February | March | April | May | June | July | August | September | October | November | December |
|---|---|---|---|---|---|---|---|---|---|---|---|
| 62 | 57 | 60 | 26 | 10 | 6 | 0 | 0 | 12 | 10 | 36 | 46 |

**Table 1: Precipitation data for Fresno, CA, in millimeters of water**

| January | February | March | April | May | June | July | August | September | October | November | December |
|---|---|---|---|---|---|---|---|---|---|---|---|
| 0 | 0 | 0 | 0 | 30 | 87 | 259 | 171 | 110 | 0 | 0 | 0 |

**Table 2: Evapotranspiration data for corn, in millimeters of water**

## Materials

*Microsoft Excel* installed on a Windows computer

**Water Budget Calculator spreadsheet file**

File name: `Farm Water Budget.xls`

Worksheet Name: `Advanced`

File type: *Microsoft Excel* spreadsheet.

## Procedure

Follow your teacher's instructions to open the Farm Water Budget Calculator. This is the same spreadsheet you used in Lesson 5.

1. Enter the information from the Background tables above into the Advanced page of the spreadsheet. Set the wilting point to 40. Refer to your notes from Lesson 6: Yield Analysis to find the average field capacity for the field. Input that value as the field capacity.

2. Remember that furrow irrigation is only 75% efficient. Add irrigation to the months where the plants are wilting or under stress, until the plants are all "OK."

3. To deliver the total irrigation needed for the year, how much water would Farmer John need to purchase?

4. Do a budget analysis for the field in 1997 based on an average corn price of $2.75 per bushel and water costing $0.10 per cubic meter. Calculate the total water cost for the field as compared to the total value of the corn harvested. (Assume that each mm of irrigated water spread over the whole field has a volume of about 400m3.)

## Analysis Question

1. Answer the essential question: *How much water did Farmer John need to apply to his field in 1997?*

# Weighing Options

 ***Essential Question:*** *What is the best decision? Consider all stakeholders, consequences, constraints, and considerations.*

## Overview

To give Farmer John good advice about the future of his farm, you need to compare all his options. Working with a group, you will need to reach consensus about which of the three options is best. As you discuss the different options, remember to use evidence to support your point of view. Use the readings from this and the previous chapter to better understand a farm's water use. Use your group list of constraints and considerations to guide your choices and eliminate unsuitable options. You will make consequence charts for your two best options to help make your decision. You will not need to make stakeholder charts. For this decision, you are considering only the farmer's point of view.

## Materials

 **WorldWatcher** *geographic visualization software*

 • *Farmer John's Corn Yield, 1997*

File name: `yield1997.wwf`

 • *Farmer John's Field Capacity Data*

File name: `FieldCapacity1997.wwf`

 *Microsoft Excel* installed on a Windows computer

 **Water Budget Calculator spreadsheet file**

File name: `Farm Water Budget.xls`

## Procedure

### *Proposal 1: Drip irrigation*

1. Use the same irrigation information as you calculated in Lesson 6: *Analyzing Irrigation Needs*, but change the irrigation efficiency to 95%.

2. Predict how you think the yield would change with the addition of drip irrigation. (Use the case studies you read in Lesson 5: *Irrigation Case Studies* to help you make your predictions.)

3. (optional) Do a budget analysis for the field based on an average corn price of $2.75 per bushel and water costing $0.10 per cubic meter. (Remember that 1 mm of water spread over the whole field is about 400 cubic meters of water.)

## *Proposal 2: Adjusting furrows*

1. Use the total water from 1997. Increase it by 20% to account for the additional water being used by the additional furrows.

2. Predict how you think this would change the yield.

3. (optional) Do a budget analysis for the field based on an average corn price of $2.75 per bushel and water costing $0.10 per cubic meter.

## *Proposal 3: Adding organic material*

1. In WorldWatcher, open the Yield 97 and Field Capacity 1997 data sets. Select an area of the field to add organic material to. Why did you select this area?

2. Using WorldWatcher, select by value to highlight this area.

3. Use the Selection Math tool [🔲] to add 15mm to the field capacity for this area.

4. What is your new average field capacity for the field?

5. Use the Farm Water Budget Excel spreadsheet to determine when Farmer John would need to irrigate this field. Use the same wilting point, rainfall, and evapotranspiration data as you did in Lesson 6: *Analyzing Irrigation Needs.*

6. Calculate the total amount of water he would need to apply to his field based on 75% irrigation efficiency.

7. Predict how you think the yield will change.

8. (optional) Do a budget analysis for the field based on an average corn price of $2.75 per bushel and water costing $0.10 per m3.

## Analysis Questions

1. For each option, calculate the irrigation needs, water use, and predicted yield. (Do this for Proposal 1, Proposal 2, Proposal 3, for Proposals 1 and 3 together; and for Proposals 2 and 3 together). You might want to make a chart to help you compare the options.

2. Select the two best options and make Cascading Consequence Charts for each of the options. Include information about cost, water use, and predicted yield.

3. Answer the essential question in the form of a report to Farmer John. What is the best decision? Consider all consequences, constraints, and considerations.
   • Make sure to address each criteria and consideration you listed.
   • Make sure to explain how any negative effects are outweighed by the positives.

# Farmer John 2

 *Essential Question: Was Farmer John's solution effective?*

## Overview

In this activity, you will use all of the information you have gathered in the last few lessons.

## Information

Several years have passed and Farmer John has written you again, asking for more advice. Read his letter and write a report in response to his concerns.

---

Dear Scientists:

Thank you for your analysis. I read all of your reports and decided to go with Proposal 2: spacing the furrows closer together. After a few more years of growing corn, I collected more data through my harvests. I would like your help in evaluating the situation. Please tell me if changing the furrow width (and using more water) improved my crop yield. In particular, what impact has it had on the middle area that usually had low growth?

Sincerely,

*Farmer John*

Farmer John

---

## Procedure

Answer Farmer John's questions using the WorldWatcher data set: Yield2000.wwf.

For your report to the farmer, include the following.

- a statement that defines the question

- a description of the steps you took to answer the question

- your answer to the farmer's questions, supported by evidence

## Analysis Question

1. Answer the essential question: *Was Farmer John's solution effective?*

# Dams

# Chapter 3
# Dams

## Connections

In the last chapter, you helped a farmer use water more efficiently to grow crops. However, the farm's crops still needed a lot of water. Where does all of this water come from? In the Fresno area, most of the water for farms comes from dams. The dams hold back the water from rivers until farmers need to use it. Dams have been built all over California (and the entire U.S.) to store water for irrigation and human consumption, prevent floods, generate hydroelectric energy, and create recreational areas for boating and fishing. In the Fresno area, agriculture would not be possible without dams to provide irrigation water to farms. This chapter explains about how and why dams are built. You will have a chance to help the community decide if a dam could be built to store more water in their area.

## In this chapter:

You will build a model of a dam on a stream table and watch what happens to the flow of the river and the area behind the dam. Using ArcView software, you will explore the dams in California, paying attention to their size and what they are used for. Dams are essential for making water available to farms in the Fresno area. The demand for water is constantly growing. By the end of the chapter, you will know enough to help the community select a location for a new dam, to increase the water they can store for future irrigation.

## When you're done you'll be able to:

*   Use topographic maps to determine the best location in a valley for a dam.
*   Make decisions about how to manage inflow and outflow from a dam and reservoir.
*   Identify major and minor dams in California, and what they are used for.

## Lesson 1
# What are Dams?

 ***Driving Question:*** *How do dams store water for farmers to use?*

## Overview

This lesson will introduce you to dams. You will read about the parts of dams and what dams are used for. The main part of the lesson will involve a whole-class activity. You and your classmates will build a small dam on a stream table and watch how the dam changes the way the water moves. As you build the dam, you will think about the direction of the river flow, how much water the dam will store, and the best locations for the dam. These observations will be important as you help the citizens of Fresno build a new dam to meet their rising demand for water.

## Important Content

- Dams are built differently depending on a number of considerations. These include: 1) their purpose, which could be irrigation, flood control, domestic water source or hydroelectric power generation; 2) topography of the dam location and 3) availability of building materials. Regardless of their specific use or location, all dams have to meet strict engineering guidelines.

- A dam's function is to hold water back, while letting out a regulated amount. They do not create extra water. They store excess water in a reservoir until it is needed by farmers and residents.

# Build a Dam

 ***Essential Question:*** *What physical characteristics must a landscape have to sustain a large reservoir?*

## Overview

A **dam** is a barrier built across a river to block the flow of river water. In most cases, a large lake called a **reservoir** forms behind a dam. Most dams have **outlet works**, a series of gates or valves that can be opened to release water from the reservoir. Outlet works allow a dam operator to control the flow of water from behind the dam.

A **spillway** is the dam's overflow channel. Spillways are used in emergencies, such as floods, to release the water from the reservoir before the pressure of the water on the dam gets too high. Spillways are often located on the top of the dam, but many reservoirs have other channels that can be used as spillways during times of high water.

You can think about the parts of a dam in terms of your bathroom sink. The drain in your sink is like the outlet works of a dam. It is the way you can control the water running out of the sink. The sink overflow holes (near the top) are like the spillway. The sink overflow holes let water out before it overflows the sides of the sink. In the same way, a dam's spillway releases excess water in case the water level gets too high.

In this activity, you will work with a group to construct a landscape with a stream suitable for the building of a dam.

## Materials

*For each group of four students:*
stream table with landscape
oil-based clay (approximately 2 lbs per stream table)
1 bucket of water
siphon or tubing
toothpicks
1 bucket for collecting discharge water
plenty of paper towels
rulers

## Safety

Follow standard safety rules and school safety rules for laboratory activities.

## Procedure

1. Set up your stream table according to your teacher's instructions. You will be creating a landscape with the clay on the stream table. You may have to work the clay to mold it to the form you want. As you design your landscape, make sure to include a section that contains high cliffs or mountains on either side of the river. Be creative in your design. You may want to include high and low riverbanks along with a few meanders.

2. After you have created your landscape, siphon water from the bucket to flow over the landscape. Make sure that the flow of water is constant but not forceful or jetting out of the tubing. On your data sheet, describe what you observe about the water flow without a dam.

3. Turn off the water. Use a paper towel to dry the area that will be a dam site.

4. Use your ruler to make three rectangles of clay measuring approximately 1 cm tall × 3 cm wide × 0.5 cm thick. Also make three rectangles of clay that are approximately 2 cm tall × 3 cm wide × 0.5 cm thick. Each of these rectangles represents a dam.

5. Take one of the 1-cm high dams and adhere it to the space you dried. Connect it to the mountains. Use a toothpick to poke three holes near the base of the dam so some water can pass through. These holes represent the **outlet works** of the dam.

6. On your data sheet, write down the location of the dam. For example, write Dam #1 – between two mountain ranges. Also fill in the dam height column.

7. Turn on a medium flow of water. *Record* what you observe, describing it as accurately as possible.

8. If you let the water run for a long time, the water may spill over the top of the dam. To prevent this, engineers usually build a **spillway** near the top of the dam to let excess water out in a controlled way. Use your toothpick to poke two or three holes near the top of the dam to keep water from flowing over the top of the dam.

9. If necessary, enlarge your **outlet works** and **spillway** (while the water is running) until your dam is full but the water level is not changing very much.

10. Rivers don't always flow at the same rate. During spring snowmelt or heavy rains, rivers carry a lot more water. Open your water hose all the way to allow the water to flow at full force. *Record* what you observe happening to your dam.

11. Turn the water flow back to medium and observe what happens to your dam. Describe what happened downstream of the dam when there was lots of water in the river. Also describe what happened when there was a medium flow of water in the river.

12. Repeat some or all of the above steps with the 2-cm tall clay rectangle at the same site, as well as in other locations. Continue to record your results.

# Dams

## Analysis Questions

1. Using your data table, describe how the size and shape of the river was altered in each of the following situations:

   A high dam is placed between two mountain ranges.

   A low dam is placed between two mountain ranges.

   A high dam is placed on a flat land area.

   A low dam is placed on a flat land area.

2. What patterns do you see in the shape of the reservoir behind the different dams?

3. Describe the function of the outlet works and spillway.

4. Answer the essential question: *What physical characteristics must a landscape have to sustain a large reservoir?* Include at least three geographic features in your answer.

## Observations

Observation of water flow without dams: _____

| Location | Dam Height (cm) | Observations at medium water flow | Observations at high water flow | Describe spillway and outlet works | River and Reservoir description |
|----------|-----------------|-----------------------------------|----------------------------------|------------------------------------|----------------------------------|
| 1. | | | | | |
| 2. | | | | | |
| 3. | | | | | |
| 4. | | | | | |
| 5. | | | | | |
| 6. | | | | | |

# Types and Uses

*Essential Question:* What are the characteristics, advantages and disadvantages of each of the four major types of dams?

## Procedure

Read the following article and answer the Analysis Questions that follow.

## Types of Dams and their Uses

For thousands of years, people have built dams on streams to enable them to use the water for their own purposes. Today, almost half of the world's rivers contain dams and more are being built.

### Dam Designs

Just as every river and watershed is unique, so is every dam site and dam. However, dams can be categorized into four basic types: embankment, concrete gravity, concrete arch, and concrete buttress. The type of dam that is built depends on the dam site's topography, geology, and the amount of water flowing in the river. The amount of water is often measured in m³/second and is called stream flow or discharge.

*Embankment dams* are made of earth and rock and are also sometimes called earthen dams. Embankment dams are usually the least expensive to build. Embankment dams are the most common type of dam. More than 80% of all dams are embankment dams. The core of an embankment dam consists of a material that is impermeable, like clay or concrete. The core is covered with rocks or soil. Embankment dams are usually built across broad valleys near sites where rocks and soil are easily found. Large embankment dams are the most massive structures humanity has ever erected. The most massive dam in the world is Tarbela Dam in Pakistan. It contains 106 million cubic meters of earth and rock, more than 40 times the volume of the Great Pyramid in Egypt.

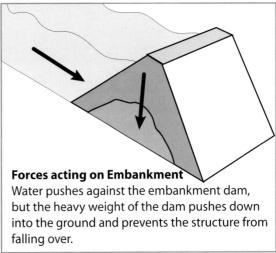

**Forces acting on Embankment**
Water pushes against the embankment dam, but the heavy weight of the dam pushes down into the ground and prevents the structure from falling over.

*Concrete gravity dams*, or gravity dams, operate under the same principles as earthen dams. Concrete dams are built where the materials needed to construct an earthen dam are not readily available. They are also built on rock foundations. These dams consist of thick walls of concrete built across valleys with firm bedrock. Gravity dams are massive like earthen dams and can resist the pressure of the reservoir water with their own weight. Historically, gravity dams have been more expensive to build than earthen dams because they require so much concrete. However, modern construction techniques have made it possible to construct concrete gravity dams at a cost that is comparable to earthen dams.

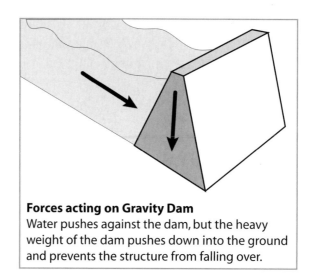

**Forces acting on Gravity Dam**
Water pushes against the dam, but the heavy weight of the dam pushes down into the ground and prevents the structure from falling over.

*Arch dams* are also made from concrete. Arch dams can only be built in narrow canyons with strong rock foundations. The maximum ratio of canyon width to dam height for arch dams is about 7 to 1. Because of these site limitations, arch dams make up only about 4% of large dams. An arch dam looks like an arch pushed onto its side. Its curved top faces upstream and its feet brace against the sides of the canyon. The way the arch transfers the force of the water into the sides of the canyon enables a thin-walled arch dam to hold back a full reservoir with only a fraction of the concrete needed for a gravity dam of similar height.

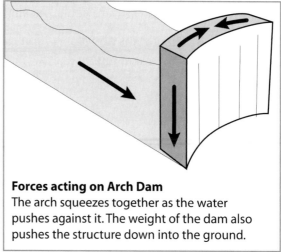

**Forces acting on Arch Dam**
The arch squeezes together as the water pushes against it. The weight of the dam also pushes the structure down into the ground.

*Buttress dams* consist of two parts: the upstream surface and the supporting buttresses. The upstream surface may be a flat slab or curved arches. The buttresses are a series of supports that brace the dam on the downstream side. The buttresses act like thin gravity dams that transfer the load down to the foundation. Buttress dams must also be built on rock foundations. Most buttress dams are made of reinforced concrete. This very expensive building material has steel bars or steel mesh embedded in it for added strength.

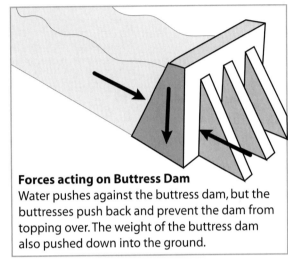

**Forces acting on Buttress Dam**
Water pushes against the buttress dam, but the buttresses push back and prevent the dam from topping over. The weight of the buttress dam also pushed down into the ground.

## How Dams Are Used

Dams have three main functions. The first is to store water to compensate for changes in river flow or in demand for water and energy. This stored water can be used for irrigation and drinking water. The second function of a dam is to raise the level of the water upstream. Higher water levels upstream increase "hydraulic head," the difference in height between the surface of a reservoir and the river downstream. Hydraulic head is used to generate electricity when water is allowed to flow through the dam and turn turbines. (Hydropower provides nearly a fifth of the world's electricity.) The third function of a dam is to control flooding and improve river navigation by keeping the flow of water high enough. Large dams also establish reservoir fisheries and provide areas for leisure activities such as boating.

As the planet's population climbs above 6 billion, humans' need for fresh water is rising as well. Scientists predict that some regions of the world will face severe shortages of fresh water during this century. Some people see dams as one way to meet the increasing human need for fresh water in these regions.

About 50% of the world's dams are built for irrigation . Between 30% and 40% of the world's irrigated land get water from dams. At least 20% of the world's agricultural production comes from irrigated land, so dams provide the water for approximately 6% to 8% of the world's food production.

Dams are an important way to meet some of the world's water and energy needs. Building a dam is a long-term investment that can deliver multiple benefits. Dams create jobs and support agriculture. They also can create income from exports like electricity and crops.

Dams, however, also have can have drawbacks. Negative effects of building a dam may include large construction costs, displacement of local people, and the destruction or modification of native ecosystems and fisheries.

In many parts of the world, the construction of dams can contribute to conflicts over who has the right to use water. For example, in the Middle East, water is a scarce resource. About 50% of the freshwater resources for that area comes from rivers that flow between two or more countries. If one country builds a dam on one of these rivers, less water flows downstream to the neighboring country. For example, Egypt and the Sudan have taken control of about 80% of the Nile River's flow with their dams. This has made countries downstream like Ethiopia justifiably angry. The Ataturk Dam project in Turkey is severely limiting water flow to many of Turkey's neighbors, whose populations experience frequent and severe water shortages. These dams have created major international disputes over who owns the water that have important implications for the survival of people and ecosystems.

## Analysis Questions

1. What factors need to be considered when choosing between earth embankment, concrete gravity, arch, and buttress dams?

2. List four reasons for building a dam.

3. Use your own words to answer the essential question: *What are the characteristics, advantages, and disadvantages of the four major types of dams?*

# Lesson 2
# California Dams

 **_Driving Question:_** _Where are most of the dams in California and what are they used for?_

## Overview

California has 1,395 dams and 1,200 of them are 25-feet high or higher. The largest 102 are at least 190 feet high and have reservoirs holding 1,230,000 cubic meters of water. These dams are used for hydroelectric power, water storage, flood control, irrigation, and other uses. In the last lesson, you learned about dam types and uses. In this lesson, you will use ArcView software to study dams in California and their function. You will use a new ArcView tool to gather information about many different dams at once. This will enable you to draw conclusions about dam types and sizes. Understanding these California dams will help you to make decisions about how to manage water in Fresno County.

## Important Content

* In California, the three main reasons for building dams are for irrigation, flood control, and hydropower.

* The site of a dam requires a large area for the water storage reservoir. Usually, dams are built at the mouths of steep valleys.

# Major California Dams

 **Essential Question:** *What are the major dams in California and why were they built at these sites?*

## Materials

 ArcView 3.2 installed on a Windows computer

 **California Dams project file**
File name: ca_dams.apr
File type: ArcView Project

 A web browser, such as Internet Explorer or Netscape Navigator

 **California Dams website file and directories**
File name: index.htm
File type: website

## Procedure

In this part of the activity, you will be looking at the relationships among land cover, reservoirs, dams, and river networks.

1. Open the ArcView project: *ca_dams.apr* according to your teacher's instructions.

2. Turn on the California theme, Major Dams, and Rivers. Notice how the rivers come together into a reservoir.

3. Zoom in on each of the dams and look at the surrounding land cover.

4. Open the Dams website according to your teacher's instructions. Look at the pictures of the seven major dams.

## Analysis Questions

1. Fill out the data table using information from the Theme Table, and from your observations in the ArcView project and the website.

2. Using both the data table and the website pictures, decide which dam looks different than most? Does the design of this dam relate to its function? If so, why?

3. Answer the essential question: *What are the major dams in California and why were they built at these sites?*

### *Major California Dams: Data Table*

| Dam Name | River Name | Primary Purpose | Surface Area (m²) | Maximum Storage (m³) | Major land cover nearby |
|----------|-----------|-----------------|-------------------|----------------------|-------------------------|
| 1. | | | | | |
| 2. | | | | | |
| 3. | | | | | |
| 4. | | | | | |
| 5. | | | | | |
| 6. | | | | | |
| 7. | | | | | |

# Minor California Dams

 **Essential Question:** *How does the Summarize tool make it easy to learn more about information in ArcView?*

## Overview

In the previous activity, you investigated seven major dams in California. In this part of the activity, you'll look at the other smaller dams. You will also learn to use some new tools in ArcView that will help you in your analysis.

## Materials

 ArcView 3.2 installed on a Windows computer

 **California Dams project file**
File name: ca_dams.apr
File type: ArcView Project

## Procedure

1. Open the California Dams ArcView project file by following your teacher's instructions.

2. Turn on the Statewide Dams theme. Notice, in general, where the dams are located.

3. Use the Summarize tool to answer the Analysis Questions. For more information about the Summarize tool, see the instructions after the Analysis Questions.

## Analysis Questions

To answer these questions, you'll need to use the Summarize tool in ArcView. In your answers, be sure to explain how you used ArcView to get your results.

1. What type of dam is most common in California? What type is least common?

2. Which purpose results in dams with the greatest average height? Why? Which purpose results in dams with the greatest maximum storage? Why?

3. Which river has the most dams on it? (Note: Offstream and Unnamed are not the names of rivers.)

4. What parts of California have the most dams? Explain why you think this is true.

5. Create two more questions about minor dams in California. Use the Summarize tool to answer them.

6. Answer the essential question: *How does the Summarize tool make it easy to learn more about information in ArcView?*

## Using the Summarize Tool Σ

The Summarize tool is used to find patterns in large amounts of ArcView data that are contained in one theme. The Summarize tool is only accessible when the attributes of a theme are shown. To view the attributes of a theme, select the Open Theme Table button 📖 when a theme is selected. For this example, open the theme table for the Statewide Dams theme. (Make sure you have highlighted/boxed the Statewide Dams theme. You can make sure of this by looking up at the window box. It should contain the same name as the theme you highlighted.)

1. To begin, select the variable you'd like to summarize by clicking on the column header in the Attributes window. For example, in Figure 1 the **Hazard** variable is selected.

**Figure 1:** A selection of a window, showing the Hazard column selected

2. Click on the Summarize tool Σ. This will bring up a dialog as shown in Figure 2.

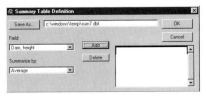

**Figure 2:** Summary Table column selected

3. The simplest form of summary table counts the total number of times a variable appears. In this case, it would list how many dams have low hazard, how many have high hazard, etc. To create this table, **click OK**. (Your results should show 596 High, 594 Low and 515 Significant.)

4. **Test your knowledge:** Use the Summarize tool to determine how many gravity dams there are in California.

## *Finding More Information*

5. If you would like more information about the summary, you can use the **Field** menu. For example, let's find the average length of a dam with low hazard.

6. Highlight the Hazard column and click the Summarize button. From the **Field** menu, scroll to find "Dam Length."

7. From the **Summarize by** menu, select the calculation you would like ArcView to perform. For this example, **select "Average"**.

The most common operations are as follows.

      **Average**  calculates the average of the data points in the selected field

      **Sum**  adds together all the data points in the selected field

      **Count**  counts the number of times each value in the selected field occurs

      **Merge**  aggregates the features of a theme

8. Click **Add** and then click OK. The results will be displayed in a new window.

9. **Test your knowledge:** Find the total surface area of all the irrigation dams in California.

**TIP:** Once you have made a summary table, you can use the Sort Ascending and Sort Descending buttons ▚▜ to put the data in order.

# Social Effects

 ***Essential Question:*** *Do the positive effects of dams outweigh the social consequences?*

## Procedure

Read the article and answer the Analysis Questions that follow.

## The Social Consequences of Dams

How much water does it take to run a household, farm, school, community, or state? Where does all the water come from? Is it always available when we need it? In fact, only about 3% of the fresh water on Earth is available for use. The other 97% of fresh water is frozen as ice. That means fresh water is not always available when and where it is needed. To help solve this problem, people have built dams. A dam is a structure built across a stream or river to block the flow of water. Water builds up behind the dam in a lake. This water can be used for farm irrigation or for drinking water. People have built simple, low dams for these uses for thousands of years.

Dams are important to many of the U.S.'s farming regions. As of 2002, about 50.4 million acres of U.S. farmland were irrigated. While farms in the midwest are mainly irrigated with groundwater, most of the irrigation water used in the west comes from dam reservoirs. Many of central California's farms get water from dam reservoirs. California's farming economy relies on this water source.

Since the twentieth century, dams that are more than 150 meters high have been built across rivers to produce electricity. In the U.S., hydroelectric dams have mainly been built in the west. The Bonneville Dam, Oroville Dam, and Hoover Dam are examples of dams used to produce hydropower. Hydroelectric power has advantages over generating electricity by burning fossil fuels. Fossil fuels produce most of the U.S.'s electricity. Power plants that burn fossil fuels give off thousands of tons of air pollutants. Burning fossil fuels also increases levels of carbon dioxide in the atmosphere. Some scientists believe this increases greenhouse effect. Hydroelectric power does not create these emissions. In the U.S., about 95,000 megawatts (MW) of electricity are generated every year by hydroelectric power. That is enough to power more than 28 million homes. It would take about 500 million barrels of oil to produce that much energy. Hydroelectric dams also boost the local economy. Dams create jobs for people who work in related industries, like electricity production and irrigation. Dams also provide another source of energy to businesses and homes. Clean power and economic growth can make dams appealing compared to burning fossil fuels.

At the same time as a dam can be good for the local economy, it can also hurt some jobs and the local wildlife. Many fishers, including salmon fishers in the Northwest, lose their work when a dam is built. A dammed river often no longer provides habitat for commercial fish species. In Washington, salmon populations have dropped because the fish cannot swim

through the dams. Other fish species die out because the dams change the flow of rivers. Fish may disappear if they cannot adapt to the changed river flow or if their habitat is destroyed.

Another social consequence of building dams is that people who live in the area behind a dam must move when a dam is built and the reservoir fills with water. This means that they lose their homes and their homeland, where their families may have lived for long periods. It also means that they might lose their livelihood, if they lived off the land by farming, fishing, or foresting. Some huge modern dams are causing enormous numbers of people to move. For example, the 138-meter (453-foot) Narmada dam project in India will displace more than half a million people from their homes when complete. China's Three Gorges dam will produce hydroelectric power and prevent the Yangtze River from flooding. This flood control could save millions of lives, but the construction of the dam also means over 1.25 million people will have to leave their homes. Another effect of dams is that some have destroyed cultural sites. For example, some irreplaceable Native American rock art now lies beneath the dam reservoirs of the western U.S.

Other factors with potential social consequences are siltation and flood control. Siltation is the build-up of sediment behind a dam. Sediment build-up can weaken a dam's structure and cause it to burst. Such an accident could be fatal for wildlife and people in the area. Another form of accident associated with dams is overflow caused by heavy rains. When reservoirs overflow, it can result in floods downstream. Sometimes to prevent an overflow as a result of heavy rain, dam operators have to open dam floodgates and release waters to save the dam. This also can cause flooding downstream.

Finally, dams result in the loss of useful water through increased evaporation. There is more water exposed to air in a dam reservoir than in a naturally flowing river. For example, the reservoir behind the Aswan Dam in Egypt loses 10% of its water to evaporation.

Because of the environmental and social effects of dams, the construction of large dams is becoming increasingly rare. Even when they are considering building small dams, governments weigh the benefits against the consequences more carefully than in the past. In doing so, they are able to benefit from hundreds of years of experience with dams. In some places in the U.S., the government has even removed some dams. They have removed dams where they believe the community and the river ecosystem will be better off without the dam.

In sum, building a dam can have far-reaching consequences for both humans and the environment. So, before they build a dam, people need to decide if the benefits of building a dam outweigh the negative consequences. When they make these decisions, governments draw on scientific understanding of both social and environmental impacts to help understand the consequences.

## Analysis Questions

1. Why would a town or country construct a dam?

2. What are some social implications of building a dam?

3. How does a dam affect the environment?

4. What are some of the negative effects of a dam?

5. Answer the essential question: *Do the positive effects of dams outweigh the social consequences?*

# Lesson 3
# Topographic Maps

 *Driving Question: How does elevation affect dams and water flow?*

## Overview

To continue your study of dams and rivers, you need to learn more about elevation. You already know that rivers flow from high to low elevation and that water does not flow uphill. So, if you want to know more about the rivers in an area, it is important to know which way is uphill. Engineers and environmental scientists use topographic maps to determine the elevation of different areas. These maps tell them the direction of streams flow and locations where large reservoirs could form. You will learn how to identify these areas on a map. You will also learn how to estimate the size of reservoirs that would form behind dams built in these locations. This knowledge will help you to consider whether it will help Fresno County to build a new dam.

## Important Content

- Topographic maps show the elevation of an area using contour lines.

- Topographic maps can be used to determine elevation and slope, and to determine river flow direction.

# Drawing Contours

**Essential Question:** *How is elevation represented on a paper map?*

## Overview

Different types of maps help environmental scientists answer questions and solve problems. In the stream table activity in Lesson 1: *Build a Dam*, you saw how water behind a dam can fill a valley. How can a scientist know (without flooding the area) where all the water will go when a dam is built? Scientists study the land to predict where and how water will move when dammed. They measure the elevation of the various areas they are studying and graph the data onto a map. This map is called a topographic map. Topographic maps contain a series of curved lines that represent elevations at the same height. In this lesson, you will learn how to interpret contour lines and make a topographic map.

## Materials

2-liter soft drink bottle (clear bottoms preferred) lump of oil-based clay (enough to fill the bottom of a 2-liter bottle) clear overhead transparency or plastic sheet metric ruler fine tip overhead transparency marker container to pour water from permanent marker

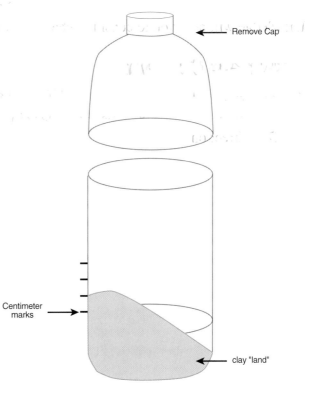

## Safety

Follow standard safety rules and school safety rules for laboratory activities.

## Procedure

1. Measure and mark 15 cm down from the top of the 2-liter bottle.

2. Cut off the top of the bottle at the 15 cm mark.

3. Use the clay to form a hill and any other landscape features you want in the bottom of the bottle. You may want to leave one area depressed to simulate a pond or lake.

4. Mark lines in 1-cm sections from the bottom of the bottle to the top with your transparency marker.

5. Slowly pour water into the container and onto the clay landscape. Add water until it becomes level with the first 1-cm mark.

6. Put three small marks on the top rim of the bottle. (These will correspond to marks you will make on the transparency sheet to help keep its position constant.)

7. To construct a contour map, place a blank transparency on top of the rim of the container. Draw a circle on your blank transparency to indicate where it touches the rim of the container. Mark your three points from the rim.

8. Look straight down from above the bottle (not at an angle) and draw another curved line on the transparency where the water meets the clay (the shoreline). (Note that this circle might not be symmetrical.)

9. Take off the transparency and add more water to the bottle until it is level with the second centimeter mark. Replace the transparency in exactly the same location (lining it up with the marks and rim circle). Draw another curved line on the transparency, as in Step 8, to show the new water level. This circle should be inside the previous line.

10. Continue adding water one centimeter at a time and drawing new contour lines (where the water meets the clay) until the clay is completely submerged.

11. The finished transparency can be traced onto a sheet of paper for future reference.

## Analysis Questions

Answer the Analysis Questions based on the contour map below.

**Bottle Rim**

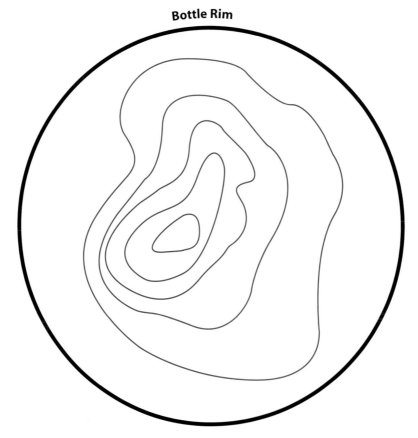

1. How many centimeters above the bottom of the bottle was the clay? How do you know?

2. Mark an ✕ on the map above where the clay was steepest. Mark an O on the map where the incline was most gradual.

3. Sketch a side view of what you think the clay formation looked like. Indicate on the drawing from which side of the bottle your view is taken.

4. What does it mean if a contour map has an area where the contour lines are very close together?

5. How are flat areas shown on a contour map?

6. Describe the different effects a rising water level has on steep areas compared with flat areas.

7. Answer the essential question: *How is elevation represented on a paper map?*

# Reading Topographic Maps 1

*Essential Question: Write a paragraph that explains to a 10-year-old how to read a topographic map.*

## Overview

In this activity, you will work more with topographic maps, so you will be able to use them to determine where a dam should be located. Refer to the map of the Deep Hole Recreation Area on the next page to answer the questions.

## Analysis Questions

1. Look at the topographic map of a region of the Deep Hole Recreation Area. Compare it to the map you made earlier in this lesson, in Lesson 3: *Drawing Contours*. Describe the similarities and differences that you see.

2. In addition to elevation, this map has markings for roads – the thin lines, or the striped line going left to right across the right corner of the page. It also has markings for rivers – the thin blue lines, sometimes labeled with the name of the river. How many rivers are on this map?

3. What areas of this map have steep elevations? What areas are flat? Explain the evidence you used to reach your answer.

4. Some of elevation lines on this map have numbers on them, indicating elevation in feet. For example, in the lower left corner of the map, you see the text Rocky Mountain. What is the elevation near this mountain?

5. On the topographic map you created for Lesson 3: *Drawing Contours*, each contour interval represented a 1-cm change in the elevation of your clay landscape. What is the elevation change represented by one contour interval on the Deep Hole Recreation Area topographic map? Explain how you reached your answer.

6. The Toccoa River runs through this map. It is shown as a thick white line across the top. In which direction is it flowing (east to west or west to east)? Remember that water always flows downhill.

7. Answer the essential question: *Write a paragraph that explains to a 10-year-old how to read a topographic map.*

Deep Hole Recreation Area

# Reading Topographic Maps 2

 ***Essential Question:*** *What can you learn from a topographic map that you can't learn from other maps?*

## Overview

Use the topographic map on the next page to answer the Analysis Questions below. The map shows the Quaking Asp Creek, which runs through Alaska Canyon in northern California.

## Materials

topographic map of Quaking Asp River Valley
paper and pencil

## Analysis Questions

1. What is the steepest area of the map? What is the flattest area of the map?

2. What is the highest point on the map? What is the lowest point?

3. Which direction is Lake Creek River flowing?

4. Which direction is the Quaking Asp River flowing?

5. Which direction is the Left Branch of the Quaking Asp River flowing?

6. What is the elevation of Quaking Asp River at the very bottom of the map?

7. Describe what a valley and a mountain top look like on a topographic map.

8. Answer the essential question: *What can you learn from a topographic map that you can't learn from other maps?*

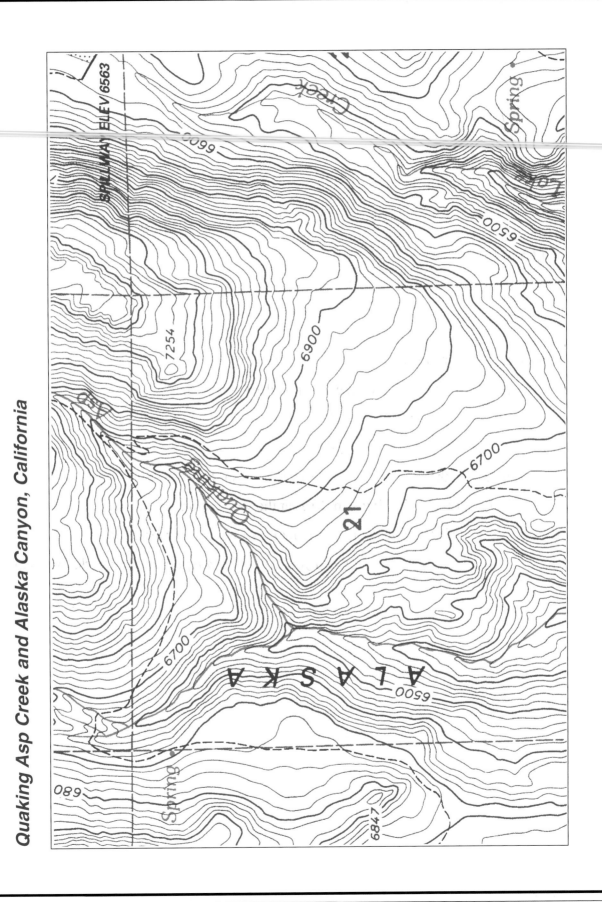

Quaking Asp Creek and Alaska Canyon, California

## Dams

# Locating a Dam

**Essential Question:** *Describe the characteristics of a location that would be a good site for a dam.*

## Overview

In this activity, you'll identify good locations for dams that could provide water to nearby farms and communities. To provide water, a dam needs to create a large reservoir behind it.

## Materials

topographic map of Quaking Asp River Valley (from Lesson 3: *Reading Topographic Maps 2*)

## Procedure

1. For each of the two dams below, do the following:
   - Draw the location of the reservoir on your map.
   - Put an ✕ on the deepest spot of the reservoir and record the depth.
   - Use the transparency grid to estimate the area of the reservoir. Record the area.

2. Pick two other locations on your topographic map that you think would be good locations for a dam. For each of them, draw the dam, determine the best height for the dam, and complete the same information as above.

3. Be prepared to share your results with the class.

## Analysis Questions

1. Which location is the best choice for a dam that will provide water to a nearby community? Why?

2. Answer the essential question: *Describe the characteristics of a location that would be a good site for a dam.*

## Dam 1: Lake Creek

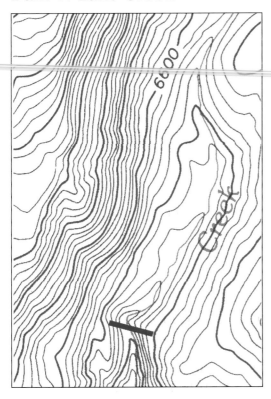

**Contour line at top of dam:** 6500 feet

**Reservoir Area:**

## Dam 2: Right Fork, Quaking Asp River

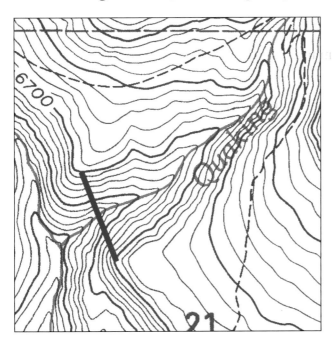

**Contour line at top of dam:** 6700 feet

**Reservoir Area:**

## Lesson 4

# Stream Flow

 *Driving Question: What is the relationship between natural stream flows and dams?*

## Overview

Now that you have identified a location and a structure for a dam, you will examine what powers them—the rivers. A dam must be located on a river and the river has to have enough water in it to make the dam practical. In this lesson, you will look at rivers and their water flow. You will analyze where river water comes from and how much water rivers carry. You will learn how scientists use special graphs, known at "hydrographs," to keep track of river water. It might be helpful to look back at your notes for the agriculture chapter. Notice the months that crops in California need the most water. Do these months match the times when stream flows are highest? Why might that be important?

## Important Content

* Rainfall is the main source of natural surface water in many parts of the world. Rainfall determines the flow (discharge) in streams.

* Stream flow hydrographs represent discharge graphically.

# Discharge

***Essential Questions:*** *What is discharge? How can its variation over time be shown on a graph?*

## Overview

The amount of water passing through a stream or river varies throughout the year. It depends on the amount of precipitation (rain and snowfall) in the local area, the amount of water flowing into the stream from tributaries (smaller streams), and the level of the water below ground underneath the stream. These variations affect how much water is available for fish, other wildlife, and people. If the water is low, there might not be enough for fish to migrate or spawn.

The amount of water flow can also impact water quality. When water flow rates are low, contamination can remain in the water longer. For example, if gasoline were accidentally spilled into the river while the flow rate was high, the water would quickly carry the gasoline downstream. That would spread the gasoline over a larger quantity of water, reducing the ratio of gasoline to water. That process of lowering the concentration of a pollutant in water is called dilution. It improves the quality of the water by reducing the amount of pollution in any specific quantity of the water. If the flow rate were low, the gasoline would remain undiluted in the water much longer. That means there would be a lot more gasoline in a smaller amount of water and in a smaller area. This could hurt fish, plants, and other animals that ingest the water or are exposed to the spill. It would also be more dangerous for people who might consume or come in physical contact with the water.

Knowing how much water is flowing through a stream can help scientists to determine the availability of resources for maintaining wildlife and for human consumption. By tracking patterns and paying attention to variations or changes in the amount of flowing water, scientists can determine how safe the water is for humans and other organisms. They can also tell if the stream is meeting the sustainability needs of local fish, plants, wildlife, and humans.

Scientists monitor the changing conditions in streams and rivers in different ways. One way is by recording the amount of water and the rate at which water flows through the river throughout the year. People can observe how much water is flowing down a river by picking a spot on the river and measuring the total volume (units$^3$) of water that flows past that spot in one second. This measurement is called stream flow or *discharge*. It is measured by multiplying the area of a section of the stream (m$^2$ or ft$^2$) by the velocity (speed) of the water in meters or feet per second (m/s or ft/s):

| Cross Section Area | $\times$ | Average Velocity | = | Discharge |
|:---:|:---:|:---:|:---:|:---:|
| (m$^2$) | $\times$ | (m/s) | = | (m$^3$/s) |
| (ft$^2$) | $\times$ | (ft/s) | = | (ft$^3$/s) |

Calculating discharge tells scientists how much water is in a waterway. During times of heavy rain and high water, discharge increases. During periods of drought, discharge decreases. To see seasonal and yearly changes in a waterway's discharge, you can create a chart called a hydrograph. (See the example for Boulder Creek between 1986 and 1995. Note the higher than normal volume of water during 1995.)

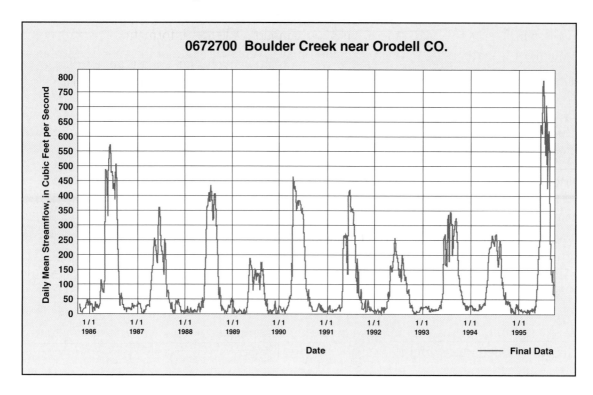

In this activity, you will investigate the discharge for a fictitious river called the Great River in Mountainburg.

## Procedure

1. Read the following paragraph.

Students at Evergreen High School in the town of Mountainburg have been collecting precipitation data for their town and the hills around it for several years. The data show that the town and hills receive large amounts of snow in the winter months and large amounts of rain the rest of the year. On average, the area gets 30 inches of snow in January and 20 inches in February. March gets only 1 inch of rain, even though it is considered a wet month (most of the moisture is melting snow). The spring months in Mountainburg are wet with April averaging 5 inches of rain, May averaging 3.5 inches, and June drying out at 1 inch. Summer tends to be the driest season. July receives only 0.5 inches of rain and August is driest, with an average of 0.25 inches. As the temperature cools, the precipitation increases. Both September and October receive 3.5 inches of rain, while November's average precipitation is 4 inches. As the temperature approaches freezing, December receives 1 inch of rain and 10 inches of snow.

2. Make a chart that organizes the data given in the paragraph on the previous page. Your chart should include the months and their average precipitation in inches. (Note that precipitation is measured by the amount of liquid water. Therefore, use the following conversion to calculate snow precipitation: 10 inches of snow = 1 inch of precipitation.)

3. The normal discharge in the Great River is 400 $m^3$/s. For every inch of precipitation in Mountainburg, the discharge into the Great River increases by 100 $m^3$/s. Calculate the flow of water in the river for each month in Mountainburg. Add this information to your chart.

4. From your chart, create a hydrograph for these data. A hydrograph is a graph of discharge and time. Put the month on the *x*-axis and the discharge on the *y*-axis. (See next page.)

## Analysis Questions

1. In which month was the discharge greatest? In which month would the river be highest?

2. Describe the shape of the hydrograph. What do the peaks and valleys represent?

3. Would all locations on the Great River have the same hydrograph? Explain your answer.

4. In your own words, describe the relationship between rainfall and river discharge.

5. Answer the essential questions: *What is discharge? How can its variation over time be shown on a graph?*

Dams

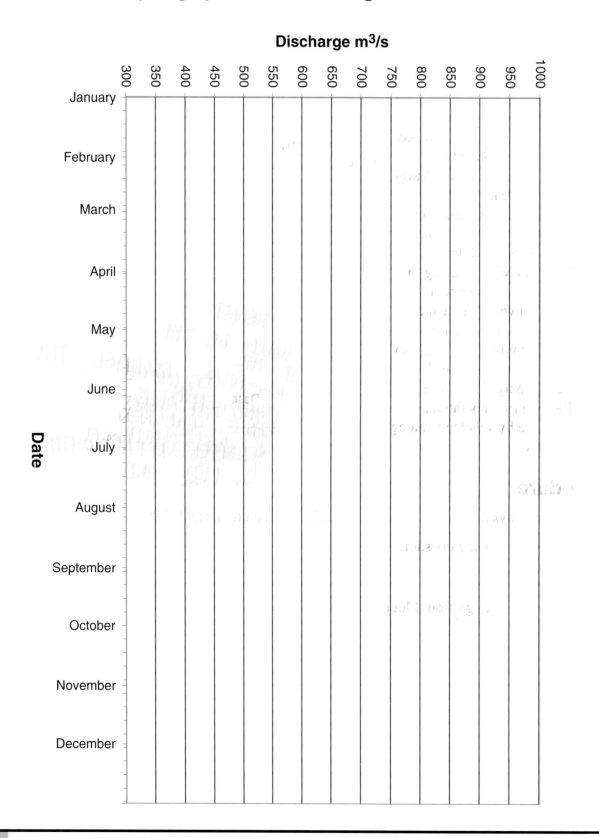

## Great River Hydrograph at Mountainburg

**Discharge m³/s**

300  350  400  450  500  550  600  650  700  750  800  850  900  950  1000

January

February

March

April

May

June

**Date**  July

August

September

October

November

December

# Discharge Downstream

 ***Essential Question:*** *How does the distance downstream from the source of rainfall and the time of year affect the hydrograph of a river?*

## Overview

In the previous activity you created a hydrograph for the Great River at Mountainburg. If you were to travel down the river 600 km, you would find a town called Desertville, in the middle of a very dry region. In this activity, you will use the data collected in Mountainburg to determine the discharge rate in Desertville. You will assume the Great River flows at an average velocity of 30 km/day. You can also assume that as the water travels from Mountainburg to Desertville, 25% is lost due to evaporation, seepage and use by vegetation along the river banks.

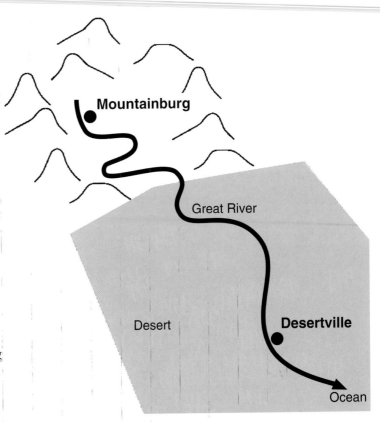

## Procedure

1. How many days does it take the water from Mountainburg to reach Desertville?

2. Answer the following questions:
   - Suppose you were in Mountainburg and placed a little raft in the river. How far away in km would it be in two days? How far away would it be in six days?
   - If you wanted to go from Mountainburg to Desertville via the river, how many days would it take you? (Assume you are not using a motorized boat.)

3. Use your answer to the questions above and your data from Lesson 4: *Discharge* to make a hydrograph for the Great River in Desertville. Do not forget to decrease the water amounts by 25% because of seepage, evaporation, and use. *(Hint: Add another column to the data chart you created in Lesson 4: Discharge.)*

## Analysis Questions

1. How do the hydrographs from Mountainburg and Desertville differ?

2. In your own words, describe the relationship between rainfall in Mountainburg and river flow in Desertville.

3. Answer the essential question: *How does the distance downstream from the source of rainfall and the time of year affect the hydrograph of a river?*

## Great River Hydrograph at Desertville

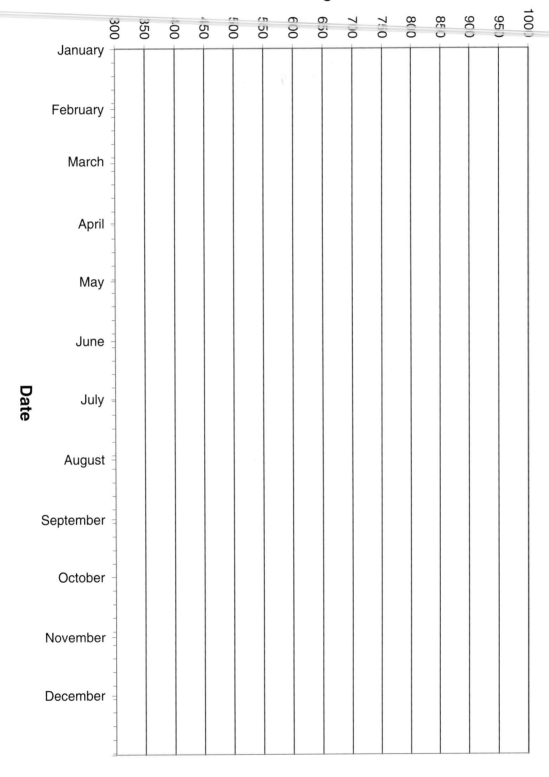

# Hydrographs

 ***Essential Question:*** *How are reservoirs and stream flow related?*

## Overview

Rivers and streams are the primary source for the water that fills dam reservoirs. Much of the water that reaches a dam will pass through the dam's outlet works and continue along the river's path below the dam. The amount of water that leaves through the outlet works is under the control of the dam operator. When a dam operator is interested in maintaining a regular flow in a river, the operator will let out the same amount of water each day, regardless of how much water entered the reservoir. This leads to changes in the reservoir's water level.

In this activity, you will make a hydrograph of the Rio Grande River in Albuquerque, New Mexico. You will also consider the effects of water flow on the reservoir and dam downstream.

## Procedure:

1. Use the data table below to draw a hydrograph for the Rio Grande River in 1998.

## Analysis Questions

1. Imagine a dam and a reservoir located downstream from the Rio Grande River where this data was collected. Based on the graph of discharge you made, when do you think the reservoir will have the most water? Why?

2. Do you think it is possible for the level of water in the reservoir to go down? How could that happen?

3. Answer the essential question: *How are reservoirs and stream flow related?*

| Discharge on the Rio Grande River at Albuquerque, NM | |
|---|---|
| Time (date) | Discharge (m³/s) |
| 1/1/98 | 924 |
| 1/15/98 | 1050 |
| 2/1/98 | 985 |
| 2/15/98 | 1210 |
| 3/1/98 | 1040 |
| 3/15/98 | 1410 |
| 4/1/98 | 1930 |
| 4/15/98 | 1160 |
| 5/1/98 | 2540 |
| 5/15/98 | 3050 |
| 6/1/98 | 2830 |
| 6/15/98 | 866 |
| 7/1/98 | 855 |
| 7/15/98 | 734 |
| 8/1/98 | 689 |
| 8/15/98 | 844 |
| 9/1/98 | 621 |
| 9/15/98 | 734 |
| 10/1/98 | 816 |
| 10/15/98 | 459 |
| 11/1/98 | 1450 |
| 11/15/98 | 888 |
| 12/1/98 | 971 |
| 12/15/98 | 824 |

# Sedimentation

 **Essential Question:** *What happens to the sediment the water carries when the river enters the reservoir?*

## Overview

In addition to water, rivers and streams also carry soil, sand, silt, leaves, and other solids as they flow. This additional material is called sediment. The amount of sediment a stream carries depends on the type of soil in the streambed, the land cover around the stream, and other factors. The amount and type of sediment can change at different times of the year. Building a dam can not only block water flow, it can also block the sediment that normally flows down the river. In this lab, you will observe what happens to sediment when it is blocked by a dam.

## Materials

*For each group of four students:*

stream table with landscape
loose pieces of clay, formed into rectangles as in Lesson 1: *Types and Uses*
1/2 cup sand
bucket of water
tube for siphoning water
bucket for collecting discharge water
paper towels

## Safety

Follow standard safety rules and school safety rules for laboratory activities.

## Procedure

1. Set up your stream table according to your teacher's instructions.

2. Pick a random place near the start of the river and place a spoonful of dry sand there. (This represents the sediment and other materials that are often carried in a river. As the river moves, it picks up dirt, rocks, leaves, etc. from the banks and carries it downstream. Additional sediment is brought into the river by its tributaries.) Turn the water flow to medium and watch where the water carries the sand for 2 to 3 minutes.

3. Pick a location for a dam downstream of the sand.

4. Turn off the water. Clean the sand out of the stream table. Make a rectangle of clay 2 cm × 3 cm × 0.5 cm. Dry the area around the dam site and use a clay rectangle to build a dam. Do not forget to use a toothpick to make the outlet works and spillway.

5. Place a new spoonful of sand at the site you chose in Step 2.

6. Turn the water to medium and watch where the water carries the sand for 2 to 3 minutes.

7. Do the same procedure at different locations for the dam and the sand. Which location moves the sediment faster? Which moves it slower?

## Analysis Questions

1. If a river continued to deposit sediment behind a dam for many months or years, what do you think would happen?

2. Answer the essential question: *What happens to the sediment the water carries when the river enters the reservoir?*

 **Dams**

# Environmental Effects of Dams

 *Essential Question: How do dams affect the environment?*

## Procedure
Read the article below and answer the Analysis Questions that follow.

## The Environmental Impacts of Dams
You have seen that building a dam across a river has a huge effect on the river and the surrounding landscape. These changes often impact the ecosystem and the fish and wildlife that inhabit it.

### Immediate Area
The most obvious effect a dam has on the environment is the flooding of the valley ecosystem where the reservoir forms. When a dam is built, some of the plants in the flooded valley are unable to survive the massive amounts of water. Other plants thrive in the newly created transition zones, which are the areas closest the shores of the reservoir, both above and below the water level. The flooding also affects animals. Animals that lived in or used the valley die or are displaced. An animal population might also be divided or cut off from other members of the population by a dam that runs through their habitat. Migrating animals, or those with large territories, can lose the valley's resources they may have depended upon. Habitat loss can also affect threatened, endangered, or unique species of plants or animals. However, dam developers currently do their best to minimize these and other kinds of environmental impacts.

Building a dam also raises the level of the underground water (the *water table*) around the reservoir. This can cause loss of plant cover in the area around the dam, which affects wildlife as well as the dam itself. Loss of vegetation typically increases the erosion of sediment into the reservoir from runoff. The sediment collects behind the dam, taking up its storage space, and limiting the useful life of the dam. However, there are ways sediment runoff can be minimized. A product called revetment maps holds down soil around the banks of the river. The mats are designed so that plants can still grow through them, but soil stay in place so that it cannot build-up behind the dam.

### Downstream Ecosystem Disruption
For some river ecosystems, periodic flooding is a key factor in maintaining a healthy habitat. The timing, length and frequency of floods are all important. Trees and other plants along the stream depend on natural stream flows to survive. Small flooding may trigger fish spawning or invertebrate migration. Without the flooding, the spawning and hatching of young fish may not take place. This flooding cycle is also important to birds, such as ospreys and bald eagles. They nest when newly hatched young fish are most abundant. If fish hatching is disrupted, it

can have an effect on the local ecosystem. When a dam interferes with the natural cycles of floods, it can disrupt the downstream ecosystems. In the past, dam managers primarily considered human concerns, such as need for fresh water and flood control in setting stream flow. Now it is becoming more common for dam managers to try to duplicate the natural cycles of stream flows to meet the needs of downstream aquatic ecosystems. In doing so, dam managers attempt to balance both human and ecosystem needs.

Another way that dams affect downstream ecosystems is by interfering with the natural flow of sediments. Sediments that flow down a river are often essential to the health of aquatic ecosystems. Sediments carry nutrients that enrich the river bottom, support its plants and animals, and shape the riverbank. Dams hold sediments in their reservoirs, which deprives downstream ecosystems of that resource. The reduction of downstream sediment flow can also affect the coastal region where the river meets the sea. River deltas, or estuaries, where rivers enter the sea, are built by sediment provided by the river. These coastal areas can be amazingly productive ecosystems. Estuaries, the part of the river where its fresh water currents mix with the seawater tides, are the "nurseries" of the sea. This is where many fish and shellfish are born and grow and where shorebirds live and feed. Without river sediment, the sea encroaches on river deltas and estuaries, washing away older sediment that cannot be replaced without a healthy flow of sediments.

Building a dam can impact the organisms that live in the river by changing the quality of the water and interfering with migration. When water is retained in large reservoirs, it can alter the water temperature. Most river ecosystems and their inhabitants are very sensitive to changes in temperature. For example, because water is retained in the reservoir, the Sun often heats the surface water, so it can be warmer than the surface water in the river would normally be. On the other hand, the water that is released from a dam comes from the bottom of the reservoir. This water is far colder than the surface water that would flow naturally if the dam were not present. Therefore, the downstream water can be much colder than it would have been without the dam. This difference in temperature can mean that fish, plants, and other organisms can no longer survive or reproduce in the river.

Large bodies of standing water, like a reservoir, are also prone to the growth of algae, which can harm downstream ecosystems when water is released. Algae can be dangerous because it uses the oxygen in the water that fish need to survive. Another problem with algae is that it sinks when it dies. Over time, the depth of the water decreases due to the build-up of dead algae. However, scientists can control the growth of algae in reservoirs by depriving it of the nutrients it needs to grow.

A dam can also be an obstacle to fish such as salmon that must migrate upstream to lay their eggs. As you will see in the next chapter, salmon populations have declined and even disappeared in some of the areas in the northwest U.S. where dams have blocked rivers where salmon historically returned to lay eggs.

## Analysis Questions

1. How does altered stream flow downstream affect downstream aquatic habitats? Give at least three examples.

2. What function does sediment have in aquatic and coastal habitats? How do dams affect the movement of sediments? What are the ecological consequences?

3. What organisms are most negatively affected by dams? How has this affected their populations?

4. Why do dams affect the water temperature downstream? What effect does this have?

5. Answer the essential question: *How do dams affect the environment?*

# Lesson 5
# Inflows and Outflows

 ***Driving Question:*** *How do farmers use dams to get water to their crops?*

## Overview

You have learned how reservoirs form behind dams and how water levels in the reservoirs are affected by precipitation. You have also seen how changes in water flow from a dam can modify downstream ecosystems. Whenever a dam is built, there are many stakeholders who are interested in the water for their own use. In this lesson, you will bring together your knowledge of dams and water storage with information about farmers' need for irrigation water. You will take the position of a manager of a dam. You will make decisions about how much water to release from the dam, how much to give to farmers, and how to best manage the scarce water resources you have.

## Important Content

- The time of year when plants in California need the most water is the time when the least amount is available naturally.

- Dams provide water storage from rivers and streams. They do not create extra water, but hold back the flow of the river to regulate the river's flow, and to make more water available to people in times when the river discharge is lower.

# Dams

# Inflows and Outflows

 ***Essential Question:*** *How are incoming stream flow, outgoing stream flow, and reservoir volume related in the model?*

## Overview

In this activity, you will use a computer model that puts you in the manager's seat at a dam. You must track several variables. Some of them you can control, others you cannot.

Look at the picture of the model on this page. On the left, you see the incoming stream flow into the reservoir. You can set the stream flow to be a normal, wet, or drought year. On the right is the outgoing stream flow. To maintain fisheries and other aquatic life downstream, the outgoing stream flow must be at least 380,000 m³ per day. As the controller of the dam, you can adjust the outgoing stream flow to hold more water in the reservoir, or let more water out to flow down the river.

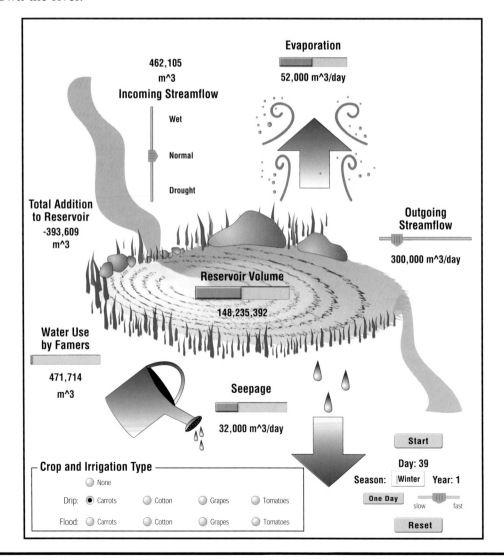

Two factors that you cannot control are seepage and evaporation. Seepage is the loss of water from the reservoir through the reservoir rim, through the dam (if it is an embankment), and through the dam foundation. Recall the experiments you did about porosity and percolation in Chapter 1: *Soil*. You learned in those experiments that different soil types allow more or less water to fill the spaces in the soil and to move through the soil. Also recall what you learned about evaporation in that chapter. Evaporation is the loss of water from the surface of the reservoir into the air. Both these numbers, seepage and evaporation, are constant in this model.

The final variables in the model are crop type and irrigation type. Most dams are used to store water for irrigation. You need to consider when farmers will need water from the reservoir and how much they will need. You can select different crops and different types of irrigation (drip or flood) to see how they affect the amount of water in the reservoir.

The controls are shown on the bottom right. They allow you to keep track of the passage of time and set how quickly time passes in the simulation.

Follow the instructions below and answer the Analysis questions to learn how the model works.

## Procedure

1. Open the model on your computer according to your teacher's instructions.

2. Click the "One Day" button once and record the values on the screen in the table below.

3. Click on the One Day button to go forward each day. Go forward five more days by clicking the One Day button five times. For each day, record the values in the table below.

| Day | Incoming Stream | Seepage | Evaporation | Water Used by Farmers | Outgoing Stream | Reservoir volume |
|-----|-----------------|---------|-------------|-----------------------|-----------------|------------------|
| 1. |  |  |  |  |  |  |
| 2. |  |  |  |  |  |  |
| 3. |  |  |  |  |  |  |
| 4. |  |  |  |  |  |  |
| 5. |  |  |  |  |  |  |

### Stop and Think

How is Reservoir Volume being calculated in the model?

4. Set the Outgoing Stream flow to 380,000 m$^3$ per day, so that fish can survive downstream. Click forward to Days 8, 9, and 10.

5. Notice that the reservoir volume is getting smaller for these three days. You can see this because the reservoir volume decreases. You can also look at "Total Addition to Reservoir" on the left side of the screen. When that number is negative, the reservoir volume is getting smaller. (Click "Reset" if you need to start over.)

6. Click "Start," and let the model run. Then stop the model around Day 6 of Year 2. (To make the model go faster, move the slider from "slow" to "fast.") Record the reservoir volume and compare it to what you recorded in the chart above. Notice that over the year, more water has been added to the reservoir.

7. If you allow the model to continue running, the reservoir will eventually overflow. You can prevent this by releasing more water (by increasing Outgoing Stream Flow) or by using some of the water for irrigation. Remember that when you choose irrigation, some crops need water only at certain times of the year and not at other times.

8. Play with the model to see if you can get the dam to overflow and to empty. Then answer the Analysis Questions.

## Analysis Questions

1. When Outgoing Stream Flow is zero, what does that mean for the river below the dam?

2. Think back to what you learned about irrigation systems in Chapter 2: *Agriculture*. Would you expect carrots grown with drip irrigation to use more or less water than carrots grown with flood irrigation?

3. Use the model to support your answer to Question 2. Describe the steps you took and the data you collected.

4. Answer the essential question: *How are incoming stream flow, outgoing stream flow, and reservoir volume related in the model?*

# Crops and Stream Flow

 ***Essential Question:*** *How do the water needs of crops relate to the water available from the stream?*

## Overview

Now that you are familiar with the dam model, this activity will give you more detailed information about the data the model uses. In this lesson, you will look at two examples of water use for irrigation and compare them to incoming stream flow. Graphs will help illustrate why dams are needed to store water to be used later to irrigate crops. Use the graphs on the following pages to answer the Analysis Questions.

## Analysis Questions

1. Look at Graph 1 and describe the difference between flood and drip irrigation, based on:
   a. when the water is needed
   b. how much water is needed.

2. Is the pattern you found in Graph 1 the same for grapes in Graph 2?

3. Look at Graph 4, which compares the amount of water needed to grow carrots with drip irrigation to the normal daily stream flow. Answer the following questions based on Graph 4.
   a. On what day do the carrots require more water than the river can provide?
   b. Instead of building a dam to irrigate the carrots, would it be possible to simply divert the river water into the field where the carrots are growing? Why or why not?

4. Use Graphs 3 and 4 to answer the following: During a dry year, at what day would carrots require more water than the river could provide?

5. Use Graphs 2 and 3 to answer the following: Could the river ever provide enough water for grapes with flood irrigation?

6. Answer the essential question: *How do the water needs of crops relate to the water available from the stream?*

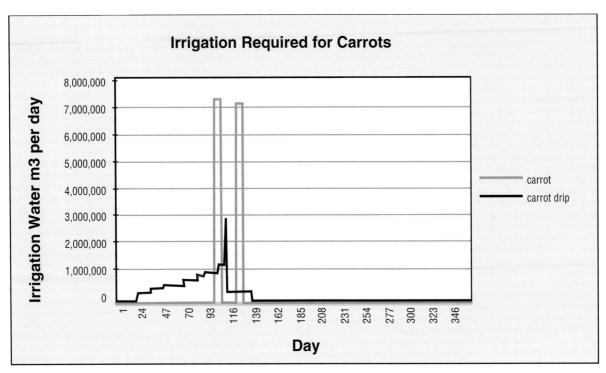

**Graph 1:** Comparing Carrots with Flood Irrigation to Carrots with Drip Irrigation

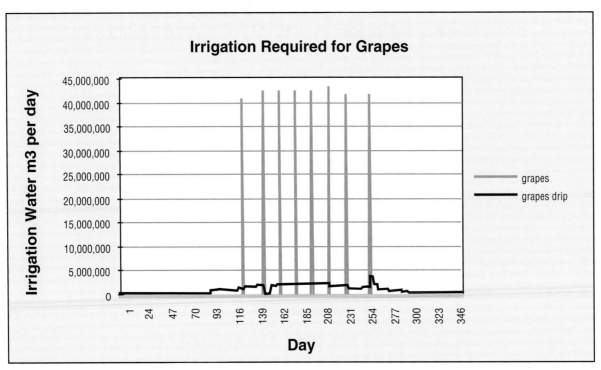

**Graph 2:** Comparing Grapes with Flood Irrigation to Grapes with Drip Irrigation

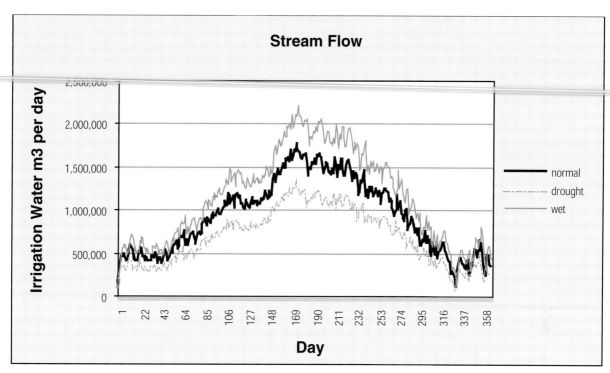

**Graph 3:** Incoming Stream Flow, Comparing Normal, Drought, and Wet Years

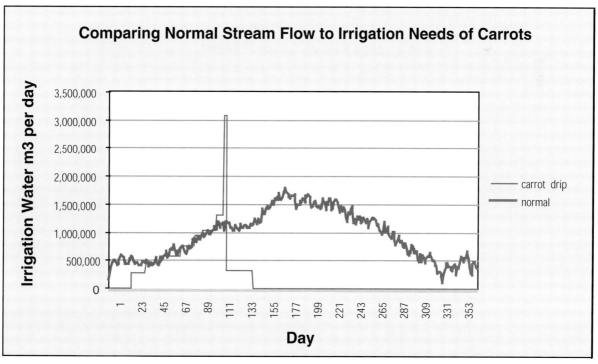

**Graph 4:** Comparing Normal Stream Flow with Water Needed to Irrigate Carrots with Drip Irrigation

# Managing a Dam

 *Essential Question: Why are dams necessary for irrigated agriculture in California?*

## Overview

In this activity, you will use the model to work through scenarios of dry and wet years with different crops. As you use the model, refer to the graphs from Lesson 5: *Crops and Stream Flow* and the graphs on the next page.

## Procedure

1. **Scenario 1:** A farmer wants to alternate growing carrots and tomatoes on his farm for the next four years.
   a. What kind of irrigation will he need to use to keep the reservoir from emptying, if all the years are normal water flow? (Remember that outgoing stream flow less than 380,000 cubic meters per day will kill fish downstream.)
   b. What if Year 1 is normal, but Years 2, 3 and 4 are drought years?

2. **Scenario 2:** A farmer wants to grow cotton as often as possible because it is most profitable. She is willing to grow carrots in other years to save water and will use drip irrigation.
   a. If there are no droughts or wet years, how often can the farmer grow cotton in a five-year time period (with carrots being grown in the off years?)
   b. How often could the farmer grow cotton if you allow the outgoing stream flow to go below 380,000 cubic meters per day?

## Analysis Questions

1. Is it acceptable to take more water out of the dam than you put in within one year? When would you allow it? When would you not allow it?

2. What do you think would be the disadvantages to changes in the water level and amount of water in the reservoir? (Hint: think about the fish and plants in the water.)

3. How can a dam protect farmers during a drought year?

4. Answer the essential question: *Why are dams necessary for irrigated agriculture in California?*

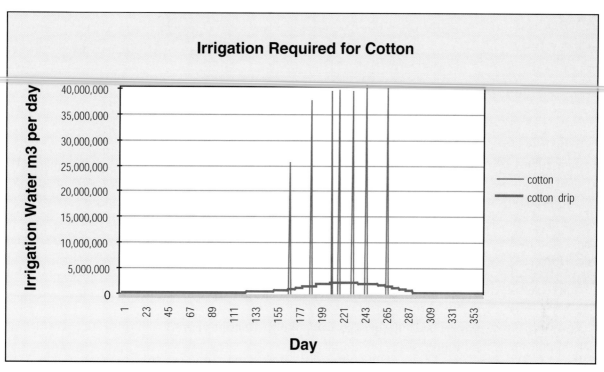

Graph 1: Amount of Irrigation Water Needed to Grow Cotton

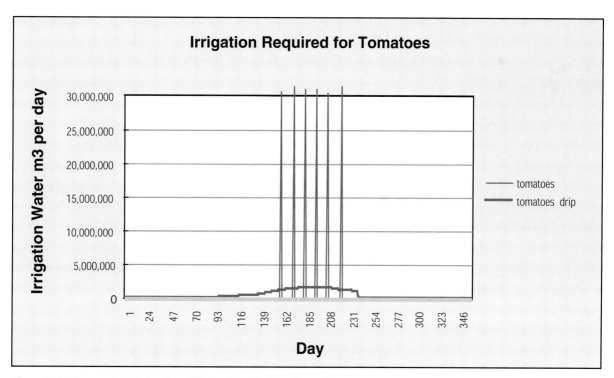

Graph 2: Amount of Irrigation Water Needed to Grow Tomatoes

## Lesson 6

# Fresno Water Board

 *Driving Question: Which location is the best site for a dam? Why?*

## Overview

Some members of the Fresno Water Board believe that the best way to solve the region's water shortage is to build another dam. They have chosen two locations that might be good sites for a dam. Your task in this lesson is to use your knowledge of stream flows, dams, and water management to select which location would best meet the area's needs. You will use ArcView to analyze and view data about the two dam sites. You will also use the Environmental Decision Making Process to help you make the best decision.

## Important Content

- Building dams has large social and political impact that is often the cause of disagreement and argument in communities.

- The site of a dam requires a large area for the water storage reservoir. Usually, dams are built at the mouths of steep valleys.

# Fresno Water Board

 ***Essential Question:*** *What constraints and criteria need to be met in this decision?*

## Overview

Your team of water engineers receives the following job offer from the Fresno Area Water Board. Read the letter and answer the Analysis Questions.

Remember that constraints describe the absolute limitations you are working under. They may be either physical limitations or limitations that come from your personal values. Some of the many factors that can constrain your decision are time, money, and laws. They also include the types and amount of environmental impacts you are willing to tolerate and may not be able to reverse. Constraints cannot be violated in a solution. Considerations are preferences that might or might not be possible. Decision makers work to achieve the most important considerations and keep in mind the constraints as they consider all available options.

Dear Scientists:

To increase the amount of water available for agriculture in the Great Central Valley, the Fresno Area Water Board intends to build a new dam. The State has narrowed the list of potential new dam locations to two promising sites. One is in the King watershed and one is in the Upper San Joaquin watershed. Both sites are northeast of the city of Fresno. Ideally, the final location will form a good reservoir that can store water for irrigation and be used for recreation activities such as boating, swimming, and fishing. Your task is to investigate these two proposed locations and recommend the best site.

As part of your evaluation of each location, you should consider the fill rate of both reservoirs to determine how long it will take before each reservoir is available for use. You should also consider the potential volume of each reservoir (how many people it can serve), potential evaporation, and the impact each proposed location will have on current land use.

Please prepare a report that contains a table comparing the above factors for each of the two proposed dam sites. Please also include a description of the techniques you used to obtain your data, your selection of the best dam location, and a justification for that decision. The table below should get you started, but you will need to add several more columns before your task is complete.

We appreciate this opportunity to work with you again.

Sincerely,

Julie Goodwater

*Julie Goodwater*

Water Board Member

| Dam (#) | Watershed | Proposed Volume (m³) | Proposed Surface Area (m²) |
|---------|-----------|----------------------|----------------------------|
| 1 | Kings | ? | ? |
| 2 | Upper San Joaquin | ? | ? |

## Analysis Questions

1. What is the Water Board looking for?

2. What factors are being compared that will help the Water Board decide which site is a good site?

3. How will you communicate your answer to the Water Board?

4. What ArcView layers do you think you will need to analyze to provide the Fresno Water Board with the information they have requested?

5. Answer the essential question: *What constraints and considerations need to be met in this decision?*

# Data About Dams

**Essential Question:** *What is the best decision? Consider all stakeholders, consequences, constraints, and considerations.*

## Overview

This activity will help you prepare your response to the Fresno Water Board.

## Materials

 ArcView 3.2 installed on a Windows computer

 **Dams project file**
File name: proposeddams.apr
File type: ArcView Project

## Procedure 1: Opening

1. Open the Dams Project file according to your teacher's directions. Each of the proposed dams is shown on the Proposed Dams theme.

## Procedure 2: Shape of the Reservoir

2. Start with Dam 1. Turn on the contour lines or the Dam 1 Elevation theme around the proposed dam. Evaluate the contour lines and select the best location for this proposed dam site.(Note: even though there is a marker in ArcView that shows the dam site, you can move the dam a little bit up or down the river if a better site can be found.)

3. Record the highest and lowest elevations in your reservoir. Use these numbers to calculate the height of the dam.

4. After you have decided where the dam should be, take a look at the potential reservoir. Trace the shape of the reservoir with the Polygon tool. Once you have traced the proposed reservoir, record the surface area by looking at the bottom left of your screen.

5. Use the dam height and the surface area to estimate a volume. (Remember that the formula for calculating volume of a rectangle is surface area x height. Although the reservoir is not a perfect rectangle, this formula will give you the approximate volume.)

6. Repeat Steps 2 through 5 for Dam 2.

## Procedure 3: Fill Time and Evaporation

7. The mean flow of the San Joaquin River is 17.02 m³/second. The mean flow of the Kings River is 11.72 m³/second. Calculate how long it will take to fill the reservoirs you created. (Begin by calculating how many seconds it would take to fill up the reservoir. Then convert this to minutes, hours, and finally, to days.)

8. As you learned in the evaporation lab, evaporation only occurs from the surface of a body of water. The evaporation rate for the two study areas is 5.2 mm per day. Calculate the volume of water your reservoir will lose each day to evaporation. (First convert the 5.2 mm to meters. Then multiply by the surface area to find the volume of water that evaporates each day.)

## Procedure 4: Land Use

9. Use the Land Use theme to identify the land that would be covered by the proposed reservoir.

10. Are there any other considerations you need to take into account before building a dam? Describe them.

## Analysis Questions

1. What is the relationship between surface area and amount of water lost to evaporation?

2. Which dam will fill faster? Is this a good or bad thing? Why?

3. Because many of the stakeholders will be affected the same way by this decision, you do not need to create stakeholder charts or consequence charts. Instead, write a few sentences to summarize who will be affected differently by each dam.

4. Answer the essential question: *What is the best decision? Consider all stakeholders, consequences, constraints, and considerations.*

   Make sure to address each criteria and consideration you listed.

   Make sure to explain how any negative effects are outweighed by the positives.

# Salmon

# Chapter 4
# Salmon

## Connections

In the last chapter, you learned about dams and how they work. As you saw, dams cause a number of environmental changes in rivers, both upstream and downstream from the dam. In this chapter, you will focus in detail on one impact of damming a river. You will look at one type of fish, the Chinook salmon, and how dams have affected their populations. You will look at a case study of salmon on the Sacramento River, which flows north of Fresno, California. You will study that river because there is still some hope of saving the salmon in that river. The story is different with the San Joaquin River, which is the closest river to Fresno. The construction of dams, excessive withdrawals of river water, and overfishing have nearly wiped out the salmon population in that river. In fact, one type of Chinook salmon that used to breed in the upper parts of the river disappeared when Friant Dam was completed in the late 1940s. This chapter focuses on the Sacramento River because there still may be time to save the salmon in that river.

## In this chapter:

In this chapter, you will learn about the life cycle of salmon. You will examine some solutions to the problems that Chinook salmon are facing in the Sacramento River. Many factors have contributed to the decline in salmon numbers. In this chapter, you will focus on the ways dams have affected these fish. You will see how dams change salmon migration, which is necessary for reproduction. You will use Excel spreadsheets to see the effects that building new dams, or pulling down old ones, might have on the salmon population. You will develop a plan for increasing the number of salmon that can survive in their changed environment. Studying the effects dams have on the environment will prove helpful when you have to decide if a dam is the right solution to the water shortage in Fresno.

## When you're done you'll be able to:

- Identify man-made and natural hazards to salmon in the Sacramento River.

- Evaluate the effects of removing a dam on the salmon migration.

- Identify the times in their life cycle at which salmon become dependent on rivers for survival because they must migrate.

# Lesson 1
# Salmon on the Sacramento

 **_Driving Question:_** _What is the life cycle of a salmon?_

## Overview

This lesson will introduce you to the life cycle of salmon. You will begin with a brief reading that will help you understand how Chinook salmon grow and reproduce. You will then use ArcView software to examine the area around the Sacramento River where salmon are found. You will graph the dwindling population of salmon. Finally, you will make a storyboard of the life of a salmon, including obstacles that salmon must overcome to reproduce successfully.

## Important Content

- Salmon travel up and down the river at different times in their lives and need specific conditions for spawning and juvenile development.

# Chinook Salmon

**?** **Essential Question:** *Why do you think dams might have a negative affect on the Chinook salmon population?*

## Overview

In this chapter, you will study Chinook salmon (*Oncorhynchus tshawytscha*). The common name for this fish was taken from the Chinook Indians, a tribe that lived on the northwest coast of North America. Other common names for the Chinook are king salmon, spring salmon and tyee salmon. Chinook are the largest species of salmon, with adults weighing up to 120 pounds. The native Chinook's range in North America extends from California to Alaska.

In this lesson, you will read about how dams affect the Chinook salmon.

Read the following article and answer the Analysis Questions below.

## The Life of the Sacramento River Chinook Salmon

The survival of the Chinook salmon population is dependent upon the health and condition of freshwater streams and rivers that drain into the Pacific Ocean. Scientists call salmon *anadromous* fish. This means they spend part of their life in freshwater rivers and streams and, the other part of their life in saltwater environments, such as the ocean. A salmon's life starts out in freshwater streams and rivers, often very far from the coast. It is in these streams and rivers where adult salmon come to reproduce and young salmon hatch. The young salmon then migrate to the ocean, where they live for several years. When it is time to reproduce, they return to the same freshwater stream where they were hatched.

The salmon's life cycle starts with a male and female creating a nest and laying eggs. The adult salmon lay their eggs in the gravel bottoms of cool rivers shaded by trees.
The female makes a nest, called a *redd*, by turning on her side and repeatedly flexing her body and tail to form a depression in the gravel streambed. She deposits thousands of pea-sized eggs in the redd. The male swims beside her releasing sperm on the eggs into the nest. The male and female create several redds, and soon after they finish laying and fertilizing eggs, they die.

After the eggs hatch, the young salmon, called *alevin*, do not leave the gravel. They have a large nourishing yolk sac attached to them. The yolk sac provides their food for about a month. After the alevin have consumed all of the food in their yolk sacs, they emerge from the gravel. They are now called *fry*. Chinook salmon fry have dark stripes on the sides of their bodies. The stripes help to camouflage them, so that predators such as larger fish and birds cannot see them. In a process called *imprinting*, the young fry learn the scent of their birth stream. The fry will follow this scent as adult salmon when they are ready to reproduce.

The salmon fry remain in the river a short time before beginning their migration downriver towards the ocean. As the young fish get closer to the ocean, they undergo a process called *smolting*. When they smolt, the body of the salmon adapts to salt water. The salmon, now known as smolts, remain in the saltwater bays where the river meets the ocean for several months. After the young Chinook salmon leave the saltwater bays and swim into the Pacific Ocean, they grow rapidly on a diet of herring, anchovies, other fish, and aquatic invertebrates.

When they are 3 to 4 years old and ready to reproduce or *spawn*, adult salmon will leave the ocean and begin swimming upriver toward the stream of their birth. During the spawning run, Chinooks undergo several remarkable changes. The male develops a hooked jaw to better compete with other males for mates. Both males and females change color from silver to red, then brown, and finally black. The heavy exertion from the long swim upstream, the spawning activities, and the physical changes deplete the salmons' energy. This is why they die soon after spawning. The nutrients released as their bodies decompose fertilize the spawning streams and surrounding lands.

The freshwater rivers and streams are important to the salmon's life cycle and if altered or polluted can affect the reproduction rate and life cycle of these fish.

## Analysis Questions

1. Where do salmon fry hatch? Where do adult salmon spend most of their lives?

2. How do adult salmon make their way back to their native river spawning ground?

3. Answer the essential question: *Why do you think dams might have a negative affect on the Chinook salmon population?*

# Salmon

# The Sacramento River

 **Essential Question:** *What are the major challenges for Chinook salmon spawning in Battle Creek?*

## Overview

In this lesson, you will study one of the negative effects dams have on the environment. You will look closely at salmon populations on the Sacramento River, particularly the Battle Creek spawning grounds. You will learn about how salmon reproduce and what people can do to preserve salmon populations in California.

## Materials

 ArcView 3.2 installed on a Windows computer

 **Salmon project file**
File name: salmon.apr
File type: ArcView Project

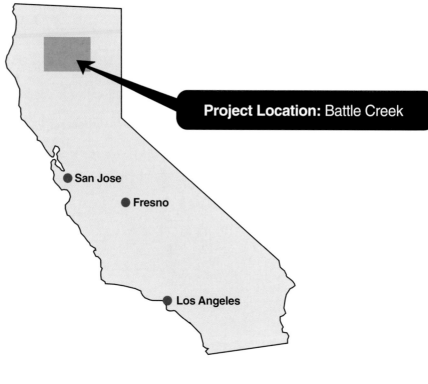

**Project Location:** Battle Creek

● San Jose

● Fresno

● Los Angeles

## Procedure

1. Open the Salmon project file according to your teacher's instructions. Turn on the Sacramento River theme.

2. Use the Measure tool, Info tool and other ArcView features to answer the Analysis Questions.

## Analysis Questions

1. How far must a Chinook salmon travel from the ocean to Battle Creek to spawn?

2. List the dams located between the Pacific Ocean and the Battle Creek spawning ground.

3. Identify any other dams on the Sacramento River that might cause problems for the Chinook salmon. For each dam, explain why you think it might be a problem for the salmon.

4. Answer the essential question: *What are the major challenges for Chinook salmon spawning in Battle Creek?* (Try to include challenges other than the dams salmon might face on their journey.)

# A Changing Population

 ***Essential Question:*** *Describe the change in the number of spawning salmon in Battle Creek over the past 20 years. What do you think caused this change?*

## Overview

The following data show the number of salmon spawning in Battle Creek over a 20-year period. Battle Creek is located upstream from Redding, California. On the map below, the circles are fish sampling sites. These are locations where scientists count the number of spawning salmon. Remember that salmon must migrate from the ocean to spawn. Over the years, several dams have been built on the Sacramento River that block the path of salmon to their spawning sites.

| Year | Number of Spawning Salmon |
|------|---------------------------|
| 1970 | 50000 |
| 1971 | 44000 |
| 1972 | 38416 |
| 1973 | 31459 |
| 1974 | 25761 |
| 1975 | 21096 |
| 1976 | 17275 |
| 1977 | 14147 |
| 1978 | 11585 |
| 1979 | 9487 |
| 1980 | 7768 |
| 1981 | 6362 |
| 1982 | 5209 |
| 1983 | 4266 |
| 1984 | 3400 |
| 1985 | 2861 |
| 1986 | 2200 |
| 1987 | 1700 |
| 1988 | 1200 |
| 1989 | 1000 |
| 1990 | 420 |

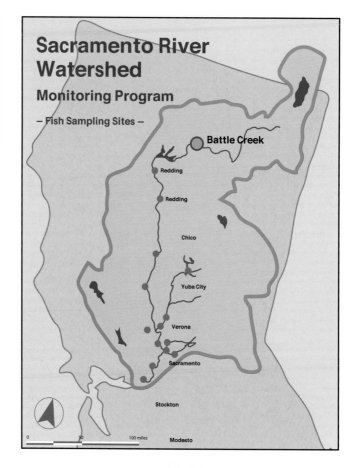

## Analysis Questions

1. Make a graph of the above data. Put the year on the *x*-axis and the number of spawning salmon on the *y*-axis.

2. How do you think the graph would look for a salmon population on an undeveloped river?

3. Write a paragraph that answers the essential question: *Describe the change in the number of spawning salmon in Battle Creek over the past 20 years. What do you think caused this change?*

# Salmon Storyboard

***Essential Question:*** *Write a story that describes the journey of "Sid the Salmon" from Battle Creek spawning grounds to the Pacific Ocean.*

## Overview

You learned in Lesson 1: *The Sacramento River,* that the journey of a Chinook salmon from its spawning grounds to the ocean and back is a long one. In this activity, you will look more closely at the stages of this journey.

## Materials

 A Web browser, such as Internet Explorer or Netscape Navigator

 **Salmon Journey website file and directories**
File name: index.htm
File type: website

## Procedure

1. Open the Salmon Journey website as directed by your teacher.

2. Look at each of the pictures on the website. In your notebook, list the pictures in the order that they would occur in a salmon's life. You might want to use your maps from Lesson 1: *The Sacramento River,* to help you.

## Analysis Questions

1. Answer the essential question: *Write a story that describes the journey of "Sid the Salmon" from Battle Creek spawning grounds to the Pacific Ocean.*

   Use information from the pictures and the readings for the details and descriptions in your story.

# Lesson 2
# Salmon Mortality

***Driving Question:*** *Why are salmon populations decreasing?*

## Overview

In the last lesson, you saw that salmon populations are decreasing. They dropped from over 50,000 in 1970 to less than 420 salmon in the Sacramento River in 1990. Why are salmon populations decreasing, while human populations are increasing? Is there a connection between the two? In this lesson, you will explore the hazards salmon face both from nature and from humans and their dams. You will read about some of these dangers and use an Excel spreadsheet to see how many salmon fall prey to hazards each year. You will end the lesson by reading about a possible solution to the problem of human-made hazards. In the next lesson, you will use your knowledge to come up with a solution to this problem.

## Important Content

- Salmon populations have been dropping drastically during the past century, since dams and other types of human development began to block their path along the Sacramento River.

- Salmon also have natural predators, and even without human interference, very few salmon survive to adulthood.

# Natural Predators

 ***Essential Question:*** *Do you agree or disagree with the removal or killing of salmon predators to help increase the salmon population? Explain your answer.*

## Overview

Salmon in California, Oregon, and Washington face the same challenges in their struggle for survival.

Read the article below about the Chinook salmon's natural predators. Answer the Analysis Questions that follow.

## A Snapshot of Salmon Predators

**Figure 1:** Many researchers see increased predation by creatures such as sea lions as one of the factors contributing to the decline of salmon. This increase in predation has been triggered by human-related changes in the ecosystem.

As you have already learned, the populations of Chinook salmon are in decline in many rivers. This is causing people to take a closer look at salmon predators as a possible key to the revival of salmon populations.

A variety of animals prey on Chinook salmon. Birds, seals, sea lions, grizzly bears, and other fish feed on them. Different animals prey on them at different states in their life cycles. For example, several species of gulls, Caspian terns, double-crested cormorants, and American white pelicans feed on juvenile salmon migrating down rivers towards the ocean. Scientists estimate that about 2% of juvenile salmon die as a result of birds preying upon them.

Fish that feed on juvenile salmon include striped bass, adult steelhead, walleye, largemouth bass, young northern pike minnows, and even some adult salmon. These predators feed on the juvenile salmon in the reservoirs behind dams.

Marine mammals, such as seal and sea lions are another predator of the Chinook salmon. Marine mammals kill and eat salmon in rivers and bays close to the coast. They eat both juvenile salmon migrating to the ocean and adult salmon returning to spawning streams from the ocean.

A Chinook salmon predator farther north than California is the grizzly bear. Grizzly bears in the Pacific Northwest and Alaska depend on the salmon spawning runs for survival. Grizzlies are especially active in Alaskan rivers where salmon runs are high in numbers. Studies have shown that healthy grizzlies need to consume about 65,000 calories a day (or 75 pounds of salmon) from mid-July until the fall to put on enough weight to survive the winter. Salmon makes up at least 70% of the grizzly bear diet during this period.

## Control of Salmon Predators

Studies have shown that reservoirs behind dams increase predation on juvenile salmon by birds and other fish species. That is because the salmon become trapped in the still water in the reservoir, where it is easy for the birds and fish to prey on them.

One response that people have considered to declining salmon populations is reducing predation on salmon.

One strategy that people have considered is to eliminate the birds that prey on them from the rivers and bays that juvenile salmon pass through. For example, one proposal in Oregon was to shoot "large numbers" of sea birds such as, Caspian terns and double-crested cormorants. This plan was dismissed because it was likely disturb the nearby nesting area of another threatened species, the bald eagle. However, another problem with this type of bird eradication program is that some of the birds that prey on salmon also prey on fish that eat salmon. So killing the birds would result in an increase in other salmon predators. Wildlife managers have also tried other strategies to protect fish from birds, such as stringing networks of wires near the dam to prevent the birds from reaching the fish.

Similar efforts have been made to reduce predation on salmon by marine mammals. For example, people have relocated sea lions away from the critical areas for salmon populations. People have also tried using loud underwater noise in these areas to "irritate" the marine mammals and discourage them from pursuing salmon. However, the populations of seals and sea lions are also in decline, and they are protected by the Marine Mammal Protection Act.

Finally, some people have suggested controlling the population of fish predators in the reservoirs behind dams and even eliminating them, particularly since many of them are not native to the region. This suggestion is controversial, though, because some of the salmon's predators are popular sport fish. Sport fishermen have strongly opposed the removal of their favorite fish from these reservoirs, particularly striped bass.

## Analysis Questions

1. Explain the predatory behavior of each of the salmon predators: birds, fish, marine mammals, and grizzly bears. During which stage in the salmon life cycle does each predator feed on them?

2. How do dams increase salmon predation by other animals?

3. Answer the essential question: *Do you agree or disagree with the removal or killing of salmon predators to help increase the salmon population? Explain your answer.*

# Man-Made Hazards

**Essential Question:** *Describe in detail one of the major man-made hazards that poses a threat to salmon as they swim up or down a major waterway like the Sacramento River.*

## Overview

In this lesson, you will continue to learn about factors that may be contributing to the decline in the Chinook salmon population. In the previous activity, you learned how predators affect the salmon population decline. In this activity, you will learn how man-made hazards affect the salmon population.

Read the following and answer the Analysis Questions that follow.

## Man-Made Hazards for Salmon

Historically, the Sacramento River has been a very important freshwater resource for the Chinook salmon population. Humans have changed the Sacramento River environment in a number of ways. How does constructing a dam or fish ladders, or altering the vegetation beside a stream affect the local salmon population? In the following paragraphs, we describe several ways in which humans modify rivers like the Sacramento and how they can affect salmon populations.

**Dams**  There are many hazards associated with dams. Dams are physical obstacles that keep salmon from being able to move between the ocean and their spawning ground. Because they can interfere with salmon movement up and downstream, dams are a threat to both fry migrating out to the ocean and adult salmon returning to spawn.

For fry swimming downstream, there is always some path they can follow to get past the dam, but they can spend a long time in the reservoir before the find it. As we learned already, the more time fry spend in a dam, the more vulnerable they are to predators. Many dam managers have installed bypass waterways to allow juveniles to go around the dam, and in some cases, they even collect fry from the reservoir and transport them around the dam in tanker trucks. Even so, many fry still get carried through spillways over the top of a dam or through the turbines of a hydroelectric dam. Many of these fry get killed by the fall from a spillway or the water pressure in a turbine.

For adult salmon swimming upstream, dams that are more than a few feet high can be a dead-end for salmon. Therefore, humans have developed an additional way to modify streams called a *fish ladder*, which you will read about in the next section of the reading.

In addition to interfering with passage up or downstream, dams can also alter a river's natural water temperature. Since water remains in a reservoir for a long period of time, the Sun can heat it well above its normal temperature. In a dam where the water is released from the top, as in a hydroelectric dam, the warmest water passes through the dam, so the water downstream from the dam can be significantly warmer than it would be without a dam. In summer in the Central Valley of California, surface water in a reservoir can reach 85° F. This warming can be a significant threat to Chinook salmon, which cannot survive for long in water above 56° F.

The introduction of dams can also reduce the amount of area suitable for spawning. Upstream from dams, reservoirs have flooded many traditional spawning grounds. Downstream, dams have caused the loss of spawning grounds by changing the natural patterns of flow. Dams reduce the fluctuation in river flow from season to season. Historically, seasonal floods from the spring snowmelt refreshed the gravel in the riverbed. While preventing annual flooding protects homes and farms, it also has meant that areas where salmon used to spawn no longer have enough gravel for salmon spawning. In recent years, dam managers have begun to try to simulate natural fluctuations in water flow with the seasons, but the results of these efforts have been mixed.

**Fish Ladders** Fish Ladders provide fish swimming upstream with a way to pass by a dam. Fish ladders are structures built to the side of dams. A ladder consists of a long series of very small dams, each one a foot or two higher than the previous one. While they are called ladders, they look more like stairs. Fish swim up a ladder either by jumping from one reservoir to the next or by swimming through a hole in the barrier between one reservoir and the next.

A fish ladder very similar to the ones built in Northern California

To the salmon, swimming up a ladder is a lot like swimming upstream through rapids. This process is tiring and may present a larger challenge to salmon swimming upstream than they would have experienced if there were no dam. Swimming up a ladder can be so difficult that some fish get swept back down or die of exhaustion from the effort.

*The construction of dams is not the only changes that humans make to nature environments. Below are other types of environmental alterations.*

**Deforestation** Another change that humans make to the natural environment is cutting down forests. The logging industry often cuts forests right to the edge of streams where salmon spawn. As you have already learned, salmon need a cool stream shaded by trees to spawn.

Cutting down the trees by a stream exposes the water in spawning grounds to direct sunlight. The increased evaporation can cause water levels to become so low that salmon cannot spawn. The high water temperature and increased ultraviolet radiation from the Sun can also kill salmon eggs before they hatch. Cutting trees uphill from a stream can increase sediment runoff from the land. Salmon also cannot spawn in streams if they become too full of sediment.

**Fish screens** When river water is removed from reservoirs to irrigate farms, the pumps that remove the water are covered with screens. These screens help keep fish and other objects out of the pumps. However, salmon fry are often too small to resist the force of the pumps and are pinned against the screen or pulled through it. Those who survive passing through the fish screen are often killed inside the pump. The rest die once the water is used for irrigation and spread over farm fields.

**Introduction of hatchery salmon** Salmon hatcheries produce large numbers of salmon through artificial reproduction. The salmon are then raised and released into the river. Hatcheries do increase the numbers of salmon but they can create other problems. For example, they can transmit diseases into the wild populations. Hatchery salmon can also introduce traits to the populations, which might be advantageous in the hatchery but prove unhealthy for fish living in the wild.

**Introduction of invasive species** Another way that humans modify the environment is through the introduction of fish species that were not native to the river. In the previous activity, you learned about fish, such as striped bass that have been introduced into reservoirs for sport fishing. Other invasive species populate the deep water directly downstream of dams. They prey on the salmon fry that are often disoriented after passing through the dam.

## Analysis Questions

1. Use the library or the Internet to research one of the human-made hazards described in the text above. Use the information you find to answer the essential question: *Describe in detail one of the major man-made hazards that poses a threat to salmon as they swim up or down a major waterway like the Sacramento River.*

   Your answer should be at least three to five paragraphs long.

# Salmon Mortality

***Essential Question:*** *What effects do dams and other human-made objects have on the survival rate of river salmon?*

## Overview

In this activity, you will work with a spreadsheet model. The model will estimate the number of salmon that survive different natural and human hazards.

First, here are some facts about Chinook salmon:

- A female Chinook lays about 4,000 eggs in a spawning season.
- The Sacramento River Chinook salmon migrate to the Pacific Ocean. They stay in the ocean for about three years. They then return to the river where they were born to spawn. The adult salmon die after spawning.
- As you learned in *A Changing Population*, the first lesson in the chapter, about 50,000 salmon spawned in the Sacramento River in 1970. That number dropped to 7768 by 1980 and only 420 salmon spawned in 1990.

## Materials

 Microsoft Excel installed on a Windows computer

 **Salmon Mortality spreadsheet file**
File name: salmon model 1.xls
File type: Microsoft Excel spreadsheet.

## Procedure

The spreadsheet model **Salmon Mortality 1** describes both natural and human influences on a Chinook salmon's life cycle. Use the model to explore the following scenarios.

1. Open the model according to your teacher's instructions. You should see an image like that shown in Figure 2 on the next page.

2. On the model, you can change the squares that are colored green. At the top of the screen, you can adjust the number of spawning salmon. Below, you can adjust the mortality rate for each of the stages of a salmon's life. When you open the model, you will see the mortality rates that reflect current world conditions.

**Salmon Mode**

| | | | | | |
|---|---|---|---|---|---|
| | Number of Spawning Salmon | 420 | (*Salmon die after spawning.) | | |
| | Number of Returning Salmon | **286** | | | |
| **Stage** | **Event** | **Mortality Rate** | | **Number of Hatchery Fish Added** | **Number of Survivors** |
| 0 | Eggs are laid | | | - | 840000 |
| 1 | Eggs are eaten or never hatch | 90% | | - | 84000 |
| 2 | Alevin are eaten by predators before they become fry | 98% | | - | 1680 |
| 3 | Fry from a fish hatchery are added in the Battle Creek spawning grounds | | | 0 | 1680 |
| 4 | Fry are eaten or killed when they pass through Coleman diversion dam | 8% | | - | 1546 |
| 5 | Fry are eaten or killed when they pass through Battle Creek diversion dam | 8% | | - | 1422 |
| 6 | Fry die because the water released from Shasta Dam is too warm | 7% | | - | 1322 |
| 7 | Fry are eaten or killed when they pass through Red Bluff diversion dam | 8% | | - | 1217 |
| 8 | Fry are sucked into fish screens on irrigation water diversions and die | 3% | | - | 1180 |
| 9 | Fry and smolts are eaten by natural predators as they make their way to the ocean | 55% | | - | 531 |
| 10 | Salmon are eaten by natural predators in the ocean | 20% | | - | 425 |
| 11 | Salmon are eaten by natural predators as they migrate up the Sacramento River to spawn | 30% | | - | 297 |
| 12 | Salmon die when they become disoriented at a dam, or become too tired ascending a fish ladder | 2% | | - | 291 |
| 13 | Salmon make it to their spawning grounds, but cannot find suitable gravel to spawn in | 2% | | - | 286 |

**Figure 2:** Salmon Model 1, opened in Microsoft Excel

## Analysis Questions

Use the Salmon Model spreadsheet and Questions 1-5 to help you fill out the following chart.

Chart 3a-1. Salmon Population Over Time

| Year | 1970 | 1980 | 1990 |
|---|---|---|---|
| A) Number of Spawning Salmon | 50,000 | 7,768 | 420 |
| B) Number of Salmon Projected to Return to Spawn | | | |
| C) Difference between Number of Salmon that Spawned and Number of Salmon Projected to Spawn | | | |
| D) Return Rate of Spawning Salmon | | | |

1. In the Salmon Mortality spreadsheet, enter the number of salmon which spawned in the Sacramento River in 1970. How many of the offspring of these salmon survived and returned to spawn? Record this number in the chart above.

2. In the Salmon Mortality spreadsheet, enter the number of salmon that spawned in the Sacramento River in 1980. How many of the offspring of these salmon survived and returned to spawn? Record this number in the chart above.

3. In the Salmon Mortality spreadsheet, enter the number of salmon that spawned in the Sacramento River in 1990. How many of the offspring of these salmon survived and returned to spawn? Record this number in the chart above.

4. Calculate the difference between the **Number of Spawning Salmon** and the **Number of Salmon Projected to Return to Spawn** for each year. (Note that Pacific salmon die after they spawn. Therefore, the projected number is of their offspring.)

5. Calculate the **Return Rate of Spawning Salmon** as a percentage.

6. Write a paragraph explaining why the return rate has remained constant while the salmon population has steadily decreased over the last 20 years.

7. What are the two different types of factors affecting the salmon population?

Complete the following scenarios using the 1990 data.

8. The Coleman and Battle Creek dams have been decommissioned. (This means they will be taken down.) This will restore spawning grounds for the endangered Sacramento River winter run Chinook salmon. Change the mortality rate due to the Coleman and Battle Creek dams to 0%. Taking down the dams will also restore the spawning habitat, so make the mortality rate due to no spawning habitat 0%. How does this affect the number of returning salmon?

9. In addition to taking down Coleman and Battle Creek dams, a temperature regulator is installed on Shasta dam. This allows water from lower levels of the reservoir to be used when the water temperature at the top of the reservoir is too hot. This is intended to eliminate salmon mortality due to high water temperatures. How might this affect the number of returning salmon?

10. To help increase the numbers of salmon, you can add alevin from a hatchery. However, to protect the genetic diversity of the wild population, the maximum number of alevin you can add is half of the total population. For example, if the population was 400, you could add up to 200 alevin from a hatchery. For the 1990 spawning run, add the maximum number of hatchery fish. How does this affect the number of returning salmon?

11. What would you suggest to local conservationists who want to return the salmon population to the 1970 numbers? How many years would you expect this to take?

12. Write a paragraph that answers the essential question: *What effects do dams and other human-made objects have on the survival rate of river salmon?*

# An Upstream Battle

 **Essential Question:** *How can dam removal help salmon populations recover?*

## Overview

Read the following passage and answer the Analysis Questions.

## A Struggle for Life

As you have learned in the previous readings, salmon spend the beginning and end part of their life in the freshwaters of rivers and streams. These freshwater environments are spawning grounds for salmon and are important for future generations. You have also learned about the affects that dams and other environmental alterations have had on the salmon. These environmental changes have contributed to the decline in the salmon population. So what would happen to the salmon population if the dams were removed?

### Dam Removal

The current thought is that dam removal will help the salmon populations. In places like Maine and Wisconsin, they have seen significant changes in the fish populations after a dam has been removed. For example, one year after the Edwards Dam in Maine was removed in 1999, millions of alewife and Atlantic salmon returned to the Kennebec River to spawn. Dam removal on the Baraboo River in Wisconsin restored 193 kilometers (120 miles) of river. The result was a doubling of species diversity among the river's fish. When the aging dam on Goldborough Creek in Washington was removed in April 2001, hundreds of salmon began swimming upstream. By fall, more than 15,000 coho salmon swam to spawning grounds that had not seen salmon since 1885.

Simply removing a dam is not the only thing scientists and engineers have to think about. River and habitat restoration are also often considered when restoring spawning grounds. Dams alter water flows upriver as well as downriver. Building a dam alters the riverbed behind a reservoir and this habitat also needs to be restored. By planting trees and other shrubbery on river's edge will ensure a shaded and cool spawning habitat for salmon. Trees and shrubbery will also help in reducing the amount of sedimentation that enters the river and affects the salmon's spawning grounds.

Dams also alter the species diversity of the river behind a dam. Some native species are unable to survive in the river after a dam is built. For young salmon to survive, these species must be re-introduced into the stream. River flows altered by the dam must be corrected because salmon are very sensitive to the water levels and flows of their native rivers.

Dam removal has had some success in restoring salmon populations. However, many other factors must be considered. If habitats are fully restored, there is still a chance that salmon populations will recover. Even those streams where salmon have been absent for years may once again have salmon running upstream.

## Analysis Questions

1. Why is dam removal alone not always enough to ensure salmon recovery? What other conditions must be corrected too?

2. Answer the essential question: *How can dam removal help salmon populations recover?*

# Lesson 3
# Policies and Budgets

***Driving Question:*** *What can we do to increase the number of salmon in the Sacramento River?*

## Overview

This lesson uses all you have learned about salmon and their life cycle to solve a problem. Salmon populations continue to drop. If we want to stop this trend, something needs to be done. You will start by identifying your goals – to increase the number of spawning salmon in the river. You will use an Excel spreadsheet to plan how you will meet the target number of fish in the river. The spreadsheet will help you track costs and estimate the number of fish that will survive each year. As you develop your plan, think about the role that dams play in the salmon story. Do you think the benefits of dams are more important than salmon or the health of the rivers? The Environmental Decision Making Process will guide you in making your decision.

## Important Content

- Salmon travel up and down the river at different stages of their lives and need specific conditions for spawning and alevin development.

- Salmon populations have been dropping drastically in recent years, since dams have blocked their path along the Sacramento River.

# California EPA

 **Essential Question:** *What are the constraints and considerations for my lobby group?*

## Overview

Imagine that the California legislature has just passed bill AB 2110, granting $2 million over 10 years to aid salmon. As a result, the Chief Administrator of the California EPA has asked groups from the electric power lobby, the fishing lobby, and the agriculture lobby to prepare a plan that will meet the requirements of the law.

Read the bill below and answer the Analysis Questions.

## Analysis Questions

1. Your teacher will assign you to one of the lobbying groups: the electric power lobby, the fishing lobby, or the agriculture lobby. Based on the group you are in, answer the essential question: *What are the constraints and considerations for my lobby group?*

---

ASSEMBLY BILL                                                No. 2110

---

### *Introduced by Assembly Member Edelson*

---

> *The people of the State of California do enact as follows:*

1          SECTION 1. The Fish and Game Code of the State of
2     California is amended to read:
3          2826 (a) The Environmental Protection Office shall prepare
4     and submit to the legislature a plan to raise the number of spawning
5     Chinook salmon in the Battle Creek tributary of the Sacramento River
6     to 800 over the next 10 years, at a cost of $2 million or less.

---

# Budgeting

***Essential Question:*** *What is the best plan? Consider all stakeholders, consequences, constraints, and considerations.*

## Overview

Creating a 10-year budget is a complicated process. In this activity, you will use a spreadsheet model to help you plan the policies you will recommend to the California EPA. You'll use the Environmental Decision Making Process to guide you through the decision.

## Materials

Microsoft Excel installed on a Windows computer

**Salmon Model 2 spreadsheet file**
File name: salmon model 2.xls
File type: Microsoft Excel spreadsheet.

## Procedure

1. Open the Salmon Model 2 spreadsheet according to your teacher's instructions. You should see a screen like shown on Figure 3.

| | | | Year 1 | Year 2 | Year 3 | Year 4 | Year 5 | Year 6 | Year 7 | Year 8 | Year 9 | Year 10 |
|---|---|---|---|---|---|---|---|---|---|---|---|---|
| **Action** | **Cost** | **Rate** | | | | | | | | | | |
| Decommission Battle Creek Dam, reduce fish ladder mortality by 1% | $120,000 | once | 0 | 0 | 0 | 0 | 0 | 0 | 0 | 0 | 0 | 0 |
| Decommission Coleman Dam, Reduce fish ladder mortality by 1% | $120,000 | once | 0 | 0 | 0 | 0 | 0 | 0 | 0 | 0 | 0 | 0 |
| Water temperature regulator, Shasta Dam | $750,000 | once | 0 | 0 | 0 | 0 | 0 | 0 | 0 | 0 | 0 | 0 |
| Decommission Redbluff Dam, Reduce fish ladder mortality by 1% | $250,000 | once | 0 | 0 | 0 | 0 | 0 | 0 | 0 | 0 | 0 | 0 |
| Reduce Agricultural water pumped from river, reduce fish screen mortality by 1% for every 1 million acre feet pumped (up to 3 MAF) | $250,000 | per MAF per year | 0 | 0 | 0 | 0 | 0 | 0 | 0 | 0 | 0 | 0 |
| Add up to 1/2 of the total spawning population as alevin from a fish hatchery | $25 | per salmon | 0 | 0 | 0 | 0 | 0 | 0 | 0 | 0 | 0 | 0 |
| **Annual Cost** | | | $0 | $0 | $0 | $0 | $0 | $0 | $0 | $0 | $0 | $0 |
| Salmon At Beginning Of Year | | | 420 | 277 | 182 | 120 | 79 | 52 | 34 | 23 | 15 | 10 |
| Salmon At End Of Year | | | 277 | 182 | 120 | 79 | 52 | 34 | 23 | 15 | 10 | 6 |
| **Ten Year Cost** | | | | | | | | | | | | |
| $0 | | | | | | | | | | | | |

Budget / Year 1 / Year 2 / Year 3 / Year 4 / Year 5 / Year 6 / Year 7 / Year 8 / Year 9 / Year 10 /

**Figure 3:** Salmon Model 2, Budget Screen

2. You can only change the data in the green cells. The Action column lists the actions that you may choose to take each year. The Cost column is the cost of that action. The Rate column indicates the degree or time that action is effective or available. For example, some actions, such as taking down a dam, will only be effective once. In each of the green cells, indicate "how much" of each action you would like to purchase for that year. As you make your selections, you will see both the yearly budget and the number of salmon change.

3. In the lower left-hand corner, a series of tabs shows the salmon mortality information from the previous salmon model for each year. You can use these tabs to explore how your actions are affecting the number of salmon on the Sacramento River.

4. On the Graph tab, Excel creates graphs of expenses and salmon population. These graphs might be useful for presentations.

5. You should develop at least two alternative plans that meet the constraints and criteria of your lobby group.

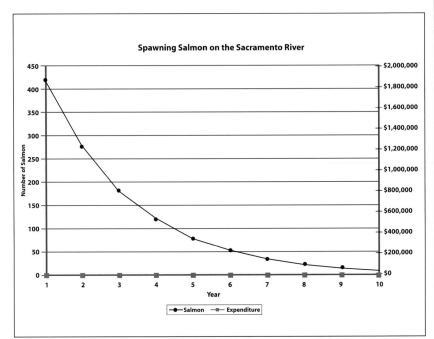

## Analysis Questions

1. Make Cascading Consequence Charts for each of your two options to determine the consequences of each plan. Remember to include consequences for the environment, the power companies (which might lose the benefits of their dams), farmers (who might lose their source of irrigation water), and consumers (who might lose recreational areas).

2. Based on your consequence charts and research, create a list of stakeholders.

3. As a group, complete stakeholder charts for each of the options.

4. Which stakeholders will be most affected by your decision? Do those stakeholders have the power to make the decision?

5. Answer the essential question: *What is the best plan? Consider all stakeholders, consequences, constraints, and considerations.*

   • Make sure to address each criteria and consideration that you listed.

   • Make sure to explain how any negative effects are outweighed by the positives.

# Aquifers

# Chapter 5
# Aquifers

## Connections

So far in this unit on Water Resources, you have focused on the relationship between agriculture and water. You studied soils and how the available water in a soil affects the amount of irrigation a farmer needs. You learned about precision farming and different irrigation methods, which can help farmers use less water while maintaining or improving crop yield. You also learned about dams, which are often the source of irrigation water. You have not yet studied consumer, or residential, use of water. This chapter covers residential water use and the source for most of that water – groundwater, or aquifers. Studying aquifers will help you find a solution to Fresno's larger problem – managing water so that less is wasted and the environment is not damaged.

## In this chapter:

This chapter focuses on residential water use. Since you are a consumer of water, you will begin by gathering data about your own water use. This will give you an idea of how much water Fresno residents probably use. You will study groundwater, or aquifers – the underground water that Fresno residents depend on for their needs. You will learn how water moves in and out of aquifers and about the dangers of pollution spreading through underground water sources. You will test water quality to see how pollution can spread and its effects. The chapter concludes with an analysis of Fresno's plan for sustainable use of the water in its aquifer.

## When you're done, you'll be able to:

* Calculate your own water use and determine ways to reduce it.

* Determine which watersheds provide water to the aquifer under Fresno.

* Calculate the recharge rates of aquifers and sustainable pump rates.

# Lesson 1:
# Human Water Use

*Driving Question: How much water do we use everyday?*

## Overview

In this lesson, you will look at how much water you use every day in your own life. You will begin by calculating the amount of water you use. You will then discuss ways to conserve water and calculate how much you could save by making small changes in your daily routine. You will also read about how people in other countries use water. You will use the information about your own water use to think about how much water the citizens of Fresno are using. Since the city of Fresno has a water shortage, it might make sense for its residents to use the conservation ideas you thought of for yourself.

## Important Content

- Conserving water involves making changes in daily activities and using new, more efficient technologies.

- Americans, in general, use very large amounts of water in their everyday lives.

# Household Water Inventory

***Essential Question:*** *How much water is consumed each day in your home?*

## Overview

In this activity, you will make an inventory of the water you use in your home.

## Procedure: Household Water Use

Your task is to determine the water use in your household for one day.

Complete the Daily Water Use Inventory Chart according to your teacher's instructions. Use paper or the Excel spreadsheet as you monitor water use in your home for an average day. Put your responses in the green boxes.

---

**Household Water Inventory Example**

Suppose five people live in your house and each person showers once a day. In the green box to the right of the word "Showers," write 5. Suppose your family does five loads of laundry each week. Next to "Loads of Laundry," you would write 0.71, because 5 loads in 7 days = 5/7≈ 0.71 loads of laundry per day.

---

## Analysis Questions

1. How many gallons of water does your household use in a given week? In a month? In a year?

2. How do you think your home's water use changes as the seasons change? Explain your reasoning.

3. Are you already conserving water at home? If so, how? If not, how might you conserve water?

4. Do you think you consume more or less water than the average household? Why?

5. Answer the essential question: *How much water is consumed each day in your home?*

## Daily Water Use Inventory

| Item | Uses/Day | Average Gallons Per Use | Assumptions |
|---|---|---|---|
| Showers | | | Assume 2.5 gallons/minute for 10 minutes |
| Brushing Teeth | | | Assume 2 gallons per use |
| Loads Of Laundry | | | Assume 8 gallons per load |
| Cleaning Dishes | | | Assume 2.2 gallons/minute for 10 minute |
| Drinking And Cooking | | | Assume 2 gallons per person per day for drinking and cooking |
| Toilet Flushes | | | Assume 1.6 gallons per flush |
| Water Indoor Plant | | | Assume 0.25 gallons per medium plant per day |
| Water Outdoor Plants or Lawn Section | | | Assume 2.5 gallons/minute for 25 minutes per section of yard |
| Other | | | Assume 0. |
| Other | | | Assume 0. |
| Other | | | Assume 0. |
| **Water Use Per Day** | | **gallons** | |

# Around The World

 ***Essential Question:*** *How does water use by people differ around the globe? Why do you think these differences exist?*

## Overview

Read the following article about three different people and the water they use. Answer the Analysis Questions.

## Naser

Naser lives in the North African country of Chad. His family has been farming for generations. He has a large family with five brothers and three sisters. Everyone in the family has a job around the farm. Naser's job is to maintain the farm's only watering hole. Naser's family and all their animals are dependent on the watering hole for all their water needs.

Each morning as the Sun comes up, Naser goes out to check on the animals and the water in the hole. He checks the amount of water in the watering hole by using a rope with many knots and a stone tied to one end. His grandfather, who still lives with the family, taught Naser how to use the rope to check the depth of the water hole. Naser lowers the rope, stone first, into the hole until he feels the stone hit the bottom. Then, he draws the rope back up and feels the rope to determine how much of it is wet and how much is still dry. The knots are all set at the same interval, so Naser starts at the bottom of the rope and counts all the wet knots. This gives Naser a good idea of how deep the water is in the hole. Naser uses that information to determine how much water is available that day for the animals and his family. His father insists that the animals get most of the water because they would die otherwise. In Chad's hot, arid climate, the animals need water to avoid dying from dehydration. Keeping the animals hydrated and healthy is essential for Naser's family because they make their money raising and selling livestock. Today, the water level is very low. Currently, temperatures are close to 90°F every day, and there is little rain. Conditions will improve when the rainy season begins. Then, temperatures will drop, and there will be 10 to 30 inches of rain over a period of three months. This will help, but the water level in the hole has been dropping for many years.

Naser drops the bucket (about 4 gallons in size) into the water hole and draws out ten buckets of water for his animals. He pours the water into a special trough that is lined and covered with straw to prevent water leakage. Water can stay in this trough most of the day. This is not necessary anymore, because the animals drink all the water soon after it is poured. Even then, they still seem thirsty. Naser's family has cattle, sheep, and goats. With temperatures being so high, each cow needs 14-16 gallons of water a day. The sheep require 2 gallons each, though the babies only need a tenth of a gallon, and the goats need a gallon each to survive. Forty gallons is just not enough to sustain them all.

Since the water level is low, Naser draws out only five buckets to bring back to his home. This is all the water his entire family can use for the day. That comes to twenty gallons for twelve people, or 1.6 gallons per person. People need at least half a gallon of water every day to stay hydrated – more when it is so hot. That leaves almost no water for food preparation, laundry, cleaning, or anything else.

Naser has never seen a bathroom, but he has heard about them from his friends who have traveled outside of their village. Taking a "bath" in a real bathroom sounds like a dream to Naser.  Once a month, Naser's family travels to the town of Abeche, where there is a community bath.

## Natalie

Natalie lives in Florida on an orchard farm where they mainly grow oranges. Her grandfather bought the orchard before the Great Depression.  Her father grew up on the farm, and so did her two brothers.  Both brothers are in college now and have no desire to return to the orchard. Her father's health has been poor lately, so he has hired more people to work the orchard and run the business.

Natalie's job at the orchard is to check the water level in the farm's five wells. Each well has an automated drip sprinkler system, which provides water directly to each individual orange tree. Each well also has a small computer that monitors the depth of the water and how much water is drawn each time the sprinklers are turned on. Natalie loves this job because she gets to ride around the orchard on their all-terrain vehicle.

Natalie's dad has noticed that the water level has dropped about 15 meters since he was a little boy.  This greatly concerns him because the water is also becoming saltier. He fears that the rising salt content may make the water unusable for irrigation. At some point, he may have to find another source of water for his orchard. In the meantime, Natalie's dad has been planting new orange trees that are genetically engineered to withstand drought. These trees do not require as much watering. In addition, he has invested heavily in a new, efficient, automated drip irrigation system that closely monitors how much water each tree needs. Even though it is expensive, he knows it will prevent a lot of water from being wasted and make the water supply last longer.

Natalie's family gets its water from a separate well. Natalie does not think the water tastes very good, even though they treat it with a water softener and a filter on the sink. Minerals and contaminants in the water supply can contribute to the unpleasant taste. Water softener cuts down on minerals like calcium and magnesium, which can build up deposits on appliances and clog pipes. The filter helps remove microorganisms, and elements like hydrogen sulfide, which can corrode pipes and give water a funny odor or taste.

Natalie's dad is also concerned about the family well.  He says they need to cut back on their water use. The family bought a new washing machine that cleans larger loads of laundry with less water. Natalie is doing her part by taking only one ten-minute shower each day. She also tries hard to remember not to flush the toilet after urinating, but she forgets most of the time.

## Johan

Johan lives in Stockholm, Sweden with his parents and baby sister. His mother is a water engineer for the city of Stockholm. The family lives in a two-story home near downtown. They do not have a yard, but there is a park nearby where Johan plays soccer in the summer and hockey in the winter.

Their house is very new with the latest water-saving devices. For example, their dishwasher uses only 8 liters of water for each load, and their showers are designed to wash your whole body in just under one minute. Much of their water comes from reclaimed and treated wastewater. Reclaimed water, also called "gray water," is wastewater that is filtered, chemically treated, and cleaned to make it safe to use again. Only their drinking and cooking water comes from a special tap, which is tied to the city water supply.

The city obtains its water from Sweden's many lakes. Johan's mother and her colleagues are responsible for making sure that Stockholm's water supply is safe to drink. Lately, bacteria from domesticated animal waste has polluted Sweden's lakes. There is also a concern that the country's surface water is becoming unsafe due to pesticide and fertilizer runoff from agricultural areas.

Johan's job around the house is to make sure the gray water recycling system has clean filters and is in good condition. The gray water recycling system reclaims the water used in doing dishes, laundry, and taking showers. It channels the water into a special treatment tank in the basement of their home. The water in the tank is then treated with chemicals, like chlorine, and passed through filters. It is then ready to use again for the shower, toilet, dishwasher, and washing machine. Johan's dad even uses gray water to water their numerous houseplants. Only the wastewater from the toilet is flushed to the city's wastewater treatment facility. The city's reclaimed water is used to water the plants and trees in the parks around the city.

## Analysis Questions

1. What differences and similarities are there between how water is used by Naser, Natalie, and Johan's families?

2. Who do you think uses less water: Naser, Natalie, or Johan? Explain your answer, using examples.

3. Answer the essential question: *How does water use by people differ around the globe? Why do you think these differences exist?*

# Setting Priorities

 *Essential Question: What category of household water use would you choose to alter to conserve water? Why?*

## Overview

In this activity, you will enter the information from your household water inventory into a spreadsheet. Later, you will have to make decisions about how you can meet the target household water use of 100 gallons of water per person per day.

## Procedure

Work with a group. Summarize each of your personal water inventories, indicating how much water you use each day. Describe categories for which group members used similar or different amounts of water. Be prepared to share your results with the class.

If you were asked to reduce your water consumption, what would be a reasonable reduction? 25%? 50%? Why? Be prepared to share your answers with the class.

Based on your household water inventory, which of the following modern conveniences are most important to you? Rank them from 10 being the most important, to 1 for the least important.

_____ showers

_____ washing dishes in a dishwasher

_____ washing dishes in a sink

_____ washing cars

_____ washing clothes in a washing machine

_____ toilets

_____ yard with grass

_____ general hygiene (washing hands, brushing teeth, etc.)

## Analysis Question

1. What percentage of water would be a reasonable reduction for your household? Why?

2. Answer the essential question: *What category of household water use would you choose to alter to conserve water? Why?*

# Calculating Water Conservation

 ***Essential Question:*** *What can be done to conserve water in your house?*

## Overview

In this activity, you will use the computer to help determine what you can do to conserve water in your home.

## Materials

 *Microsoft Excel* installed on a Windows computer

 **Water Conservation spreadsheet file**

File name: `water conservation.xls`

File type: *Microsoft Excel* spreadsheet.

## Procedure

1. Open up the Water Conservation spreadsheet according to your teacher's instructions.

2. In the blue cells, enter your average daily water usage (from Lesson 1: *Household Water Inventory*). Also enter your target conservation percentage (from Lesson 1: *Setting Priorities*).

3. In the green cells, change the uses/day for each of the major water uses in your house. In the yellow cells, change the amount of water per use. For each change from your current daily household use, be prepared to explain your reasons for making the change.

| | Water Conservation.xls | | |
|---|---|---|---|
| | A | B | C | D |
| 1 | | | | |
| 2 | **Estimated Daily Water Use** | **329** | gallons | (From *HWU1a: Household Inventory* ) |
| 3 | Target Conservation | 25% | | (From *HWU1b: Setting Priorities* ) |
| 4 | Target Water Use Per Day | **246.75** | gallons | |
| 5 | | | | |
| 6 | **Item** | **Uses/Day** | **Average Gallons Per Use** | **Assumptions** |
| 7 | Showers | 4 | 25 | Assume 2.5 gallons/minute for 10 minutes |
| 8 | Brushing Teeth | 4 | 2 | Assume 2 gallons per use |
| 9 | Loads Of Laundry | 3 | 8 | Assume 8 gallons per load |
| 10 | Cleaning Dishes | 2 | 22 | Assume 2.2 gallons/minute for 10 minute |
| 11 | Drinking And Cooking | 4 | 2 | Assume 2 gallons per person per day for drinking and cooking |
| 12 | Toilet Flushes | 12 | 1.6 | Assume 1.6 gallons per flush |
| 13 | Water Indoor Plant | 5 | 0.25 | Assume 0.25 gallons per medium plant per day |
| 14 | Water Outdoor Plants or Lawn Section | 2 | 62.5 | Assume 2.5 gallons/minute for 25 minutes per section of yard |
| 15 | Other | | 0 | Assume 0. |
| 16 | Other | | 0 | Assume 0. |
| 17 | Other | | 0 | Assume 0. |
| 18 | **Water Use Per Day** | 329 | gallons | |

4. Be prepared to share your conservation strategy with the class.

## Analysis Questions

1. Based on your Water Conservation spreadsheet, which conserves more water: changing the number in the Uses Per Day column or installing efficient technologies that alter the Average Gallons per Use column?

2. Compare your results with those from your inventory created in Lesson 1: *Household Water Inventory*. Which of the conveniences listed required the greatest sacrifice?

3. Answer the essential question: *What can be done to conserve water in your house?*

# Lesson 2:
# Aquifer Basics

***Driving Question:*** *Where does groundwater come from and how do we collect it?*

## Overview

In the last lesson, you looked at how much water you use every day, and compared it to water use by people in other countries. In this lesson, you will again focus on Fresno's water problems. Most of Fresno's water comes from an underground area where water accumulates called an aquifer. This lesson introduces you to aquifers. You will build a model of an aquifer in class and see demonstrations of how water moves underground. In later lessons, you will see how the overuse of underground water can affect both the aquifer and life on the surface.

## Important Content

- Aquifers are underground water storage, where the water is held in pore spaces between rocks, gravel, and soil.

- Layers of soil and rock underground can either allow water to flow, or can act as confining layers and prevent water movement.

# Under the Ground

***Essential Question:*** *Where do you think water is located under the ground?*

## Overview

We all bring different ideas to science class about the way things work. In this activity, you will discuss some of those ideas to determine where you need to focus your learning.

## Procedure

1. Draw a diagram of what you think the earth under your feet looks like. Label those parts where you think you would find soil, rocks, water, and other materials.

2. Describe and explain your drawing in about three sentences.

3. Think back to the activity on porosity in the soil chapter (Chapter 1, Lesson 4: *Porosity*), where you studied the porosity of different soil types. How do you think porosity might affect where water is found underground?

4. Answer the essential question: *Where do you think water is located under the ground?*

# Building an Aquifer

 ***Essential Question:*** *In your own words, define and describe an aquifer.*

## Overview

When you worked on your precision farming project, your focus was on getting water to the plants. At the time, you were not asked to consider what happened to the water the plants did not use. You know that much of the water seeped into the ground, but then what? Some of it continued down through the soil to deeper layers and then into groundwater. In this activity, you are going to build a model to show what groundwater looks like—an aquifer. An aquifer is not an underground lake, as many people think. Actually, groundwater exists in tiny spaces between rocks, sand, and soil. As you build your model, think about how water might move through it.

## Materials

clear plastic cup

gravel or small rocks

clay

sand

small cup of blue colored water

small cup of red colored water

## Safety

Follow standard safety rules and school safety rules for laboratory activities.

## Procedure

1. Fill one clear cup 1/3 full with gravel. Add blue water until half of the gravel is covered.

2. Put a layer of clay over the gravel, sealing it off from the rest of the cup. Add sand until the cup is 2/3 full. Construct land features (hills, mountains, valleys, etc) with the clay and sand.

3. Pour red water slowly into the cup until it reaches the top of the gravel or sand.

## Analysis Questions

1. Did any of the water that you poured on the sand make it to the gravel layer below the clay? Why or why not?

2. Groundwater fills the pore spaces between soil or rock particles. Pore spaces that are completely filled by water are called saturated zones. Areas that may be wet but are not completely filled are called unsaturated zones. Draw a diagram of your cup and label the saturated and unsaturated zones.

3. In this activity, the blue water layer represents an **aquifer**. Answer the essential question: *In your own words, define and describe an aquifer.*

# Demonstrations

***Essential Question:*** *Are aquifers underground lakes? Why or why not?*

## Overview

In the last activity, you built a model aquifer. Your aquifer showed that sometimes underground water is easily accessible. Other times, it can be deep under the ground, trapped under layers of rocks or clay. The amount and location of water underground is related to the water on the surface, and vice versa. In this lesson, you will look at these relationships and define some of the terms scientists use to describe groundwater.

## Procedure

As your teacher demonstrates each of the following principles, describe them in your own words.

1. water table

2. confining layer

3. confined aquifer

4. unconfined aquifer

5. recharge zone

6. aquifer

7. cone of depression

## Analysis Questions

1. What happens when water seeps through the soil to a confining layer?

2. Answer the essential question: *Are aquifers underground lakes? Why or why not?*

# Parts of Aquifers

*Essential Question: How are a water table and an aquifer related?*

## Overview

This activity helps you pull together some of the information you have learned about aquifers.

## Analysis Questions

1. Label the following on the picture below: confining layer, confined aquifer, unconfined aquifer, saturated zone, unsaturated zone.

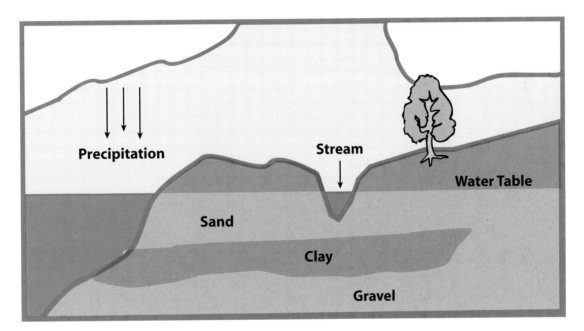

2. Will the precipitation falling on the left side of the picture (down arrows) flow into the gravel aquifer? Why or why not?

3. If there is a farm to the right of the tree, identify three places in the picture where you might find water that came from the farm.

4. If someone dug a hole next to the tree that went 2 feet deeper than the water table, what would they see?

5. Answer the essential question: *How are a water table and an aquifer related?*

# Aquifer Summary

***Essential Question:*** *How is water stored underground?*

## Overview

In the last few activities, you built a model of an aquifer and identified its parts. In this reading, you will learn how water gets into aquifers, which is also known as 'recharging'. Read the following article to find out the various ways aquifers recharge.

## How Groundwater Accumulates

Many people have difficulty picturing what a large body of underground water would look like. You may have an image of groundwater collecting in underground lakes or flowing in underground rivers. While there are underground lakes and waters, most underground water is contained in relatively small gaps in rocks and soil.

Probably the best way to imagine groundwater is to think of it as water in a sponge. Only in this case, the sponge is an underground layer of rock and soil. Groundwater is the water below the surface that saturates (or fills) the pores or cracks in the rocks and soil. This water-saturated area is called an aquifer.

So, how does water reach an aquifer? We will start our description of this portion of the water cycle with precipitation. When rain falls or snow melts, some of the water evaporates, some flows over land and collects in streams, rivers, ponds, or lakes, and some infiltrates into the ground, into the pores or cracks in soil and rocks.

When water enters the soil, it is usually retained within the top layer. As that layer starts to reach saturation, more and more water flows down through it toward the underlying aquifer. However, there is another area between the land surface and the aquifer that water travels through first. Hydrologists, scientists who study the movement of water, call this area the unsaturated zone, in contrast to the aquifer which is saturated. Just like the soil that you studied earlier, the unsaturated zone usually contains some water. In normal circumstances, the only time an unsaturated zone becomes saturated is after a heavy rainfall or snow melt, while the water from above passes through it.

### Filling the Aquifer

Below the unsaturated zone is the water table. *Water table* is the name that scientists use to describe the top of the saturated zone that makes up an aquifer. Below the water table, all the pore spaces between the gravel and sand particles in the rocks are full of water. When the water table rises, that means the aquifer is getting filled more quickly than it is being drained. When the water table is rising, that means that the aquifer is being *recharged*. When the water table falls, that means the aquifer is losing water more quickly than it is being refilled.

Natural recharge of aquifers is a slow process because groundwater moves slowly through the unsaturated zone and the aquifer. For example, there is an aquifer underlying the High Plains from Texas to Canada. This is an area of low precipitation. If it were emptied, it would take hundreds or even thousands of years to refill at present recharge rates. In contrast, a shallow aquifer in an area of high precipitation may be refilled within a few years.

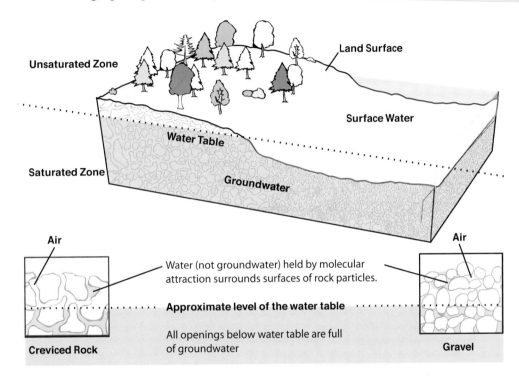

## Water for Wells

A well operates like a large pore in an aquifer with a pipe leading to the surface. A well that has been dug or drilled into saturated rocks will fill with water to about the level of the water table. You might think of the well as being like a straw inserted into a cup. The liquid inside the cup fills the straw to the level of the liquid in the cup. When water is pumped from a well, it is like liquid being sucked through the straw. It will draw water from the saturated rocks into the well to replace the pumped water.

However, in some cases, water may not be able to flow into a well from an aquifer as quickly as it is being removed. To maintain a constant supply of water, the water must be able to move through the aquifer as quickly as the water is being drawn up the well. Some rock, such as clay or solid granite, may have only a few small cracks for water to move through. Such rocks transmit only small quantities of water and do not make good aquifers for wells. Rocks such as sandstone and cavernous limestone have large connected openings that permit water to move more freely. Since aquifers made of these rocks transmit larger quantities of water, they make good sites for wells. Depending on the type of aquifer, the flow of water from a well can range anywhere from a few hundred gallons a day to several million gallons a day.

## Analysis Questions

1. Where does the water found in an aquifer come from?

2. In Chapter 1, Lesson 5: *Available Water*, you learned about wilting point, available water, and porosity. Relate what you have read above to each of those concepts. Write at least three sentences for each.

3 What factors affect how much water people get from a well?

4 Answer the essential question: *How is water stored underground?*

# Lesson 3:
# Withdrawing Water from Aquifers

 ***Driving Question:*** *How is water removed from an aquifer? What effects can that have on the surface?*

## Overview

In the last two lessons, you explored your own water use and ways of conserving water. Then, you learned about one source of water, aquifers, and how they work. Many people, including the residents of Fresno, get most of their water from underground storage, or aquifers. Just like other water sources, aquifers have a limited amount of water. In this lesson, you will explore how water is removed from aquifers. You will see some of the effects of withdrawing too much water from an aquifer. Most aquifers are large, but people do not understand their capacity. We have a tendency to take more water out of an aquifer than what goes in. Overdraft, which is the withdrawal of water from aquifers more rapidly than it can be recharged, may continue for several years without much damage. After a while, however, damage occurs and we have to deal with the consequences.

## Important Content

- People use wells to remove water from the ground.

- In many places, water is taken out of aquifers faster than it can be replaced. This can cause sinkholes, land subsidence, saltwater intrusion, and/or increased salinity of water.

# Wells

*Essential Question:* What are some things to consider when digging a well?

## Overview

As you have already seen, water is one of our essential resources. Humans need water to survive. While there are many different sources of fresh water, about 97% of the world's fresh water comes from underground. Tapping into this natural resource is often a community's most efficient way of obtaining water, and the best way of accessing this water is usually by drilling wells. People use various types of wells to get water out of the ground. Many factors, such as the safety of the location, must be considered when deciding to dig a well. In the following reading, you will read about different kinds of wells and technological advances in well construction.

## The History of Wells

Humans have been digging wells for water for thousands of years. The earliest wells were dug by hand. People simply dug straight down until they reached the water table, and water would fill the bottom of the hole. Then, water was brought to the surface by a container raised and lowered at the end of a cord.

Wells can be dug with the simplest equipment. However, there are two important limitations to digging wells. First, there is a practical limit to how deep a well can be dug, and second, a well can only be dug through relatively soft ground. Therefore, in modern times, most wells are drilled, not dug. A well can be drilled to a much greater depth for the same cost in comparison to digging. In addition, a drill can pass through solid rock. Drills can be powered by hand, but today most drills are powered by a machine.

Another advance in wells came with the introduction of the pump. For hundreds of years, pumps were powered by hand, but today nearly all pumps are powered by machines. A pump works by sucking water up through a pipe, similar to the way a person sucks water up through a straw.

Except for the introduction of drilling and pumping, a modern well is the same as an ancient well. A well is still a hole in the ground through which people raise underground water to the surface.

## Analysis Questions

1. How were the first wells dug?

2. What are the benefits of drilled wells?

3. Answer the essential question: *What are some things to consider when digging a well?*

# Withdrawing Water

 **Essential Question:** *What happens if we take more water from an aquifer than what goes into it?*

## Overview

In this activity, you will analyze a graph that shows how much water is stored in an aquifer. Water managers use graphs like this to predict the amount of water they can remove from an aquifer each year. Study the graph and answer the Analysis Questions that follow.

## Procedure

The graph below shows the water stored by an aquifer beneath a small town in Texas. It is a farming town that suffered through a drought in the mid-1970s but recovered soon after. Now the population is booming. There is increased demand for water for new housing developments, industry, and for irrigation.

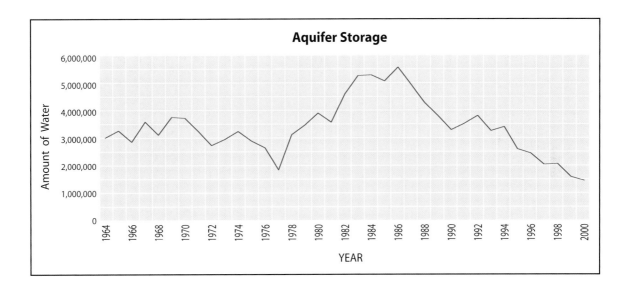

## Analysis Questions

1. How did the drought in the 1970s affect the amount of water in the aquifer? What evidence is there in the graph to support your claims?

2. At what other times has the water level in the aquifer gone down? What could account for this decline?

3. Assume that the trend from 1986 to 2000 is repeated between 2000 and 2015. Sketch a graph of water storage in this aquifer between 2000 and 2015.

4. If the amount of water declines to zero, what will happen to the wells in this Texas town?

5. Do you think development (housing and industry) should be restricted in this town to preserve the water supply? If not, what would you do about the problem?

6. Answer the essential question: *What happens if we take more water out of an aquifer than what goes into it?*

# Effects of Drawdown

 ***Essential Question:*** *Why should we be concerned about aquifer drawdown?*

## Overview

Sometimes, withdrawing water from aquifers has effects other than just reducing the amount of water in the aquifer. These effects can even be seen on the surface. Read the following and answer the Analysis Questions.

## Aquifer Drawdown and Its Effects

Because the water in an aquifer is constantly moving, the water level in aquifers is not the same at all times or even at all locations in the aquifer. Seasonal variation in rainfall and long-term drought are two natural patterns that can affect the amount of water in the aquifer. The amount of water withdrawn through wells can also change an aquifer's water level. Larger wells may withdraw thousands of gallons of water per hour. This is clearly an unnatural change in the groundwater system.

When the water table drops below the bottom of a well, the well becomes overdrawn, or has "dried up." When this happens, individuals or communities must dig a deeper well or find another source of water. Overdrawing wells is not the only problem that can result from drawing water too quickly from an aquifer. Overdrawing can also cause *cones of depression, saltwater intrusion* and *land subsidence*. Each of these processes is described below.

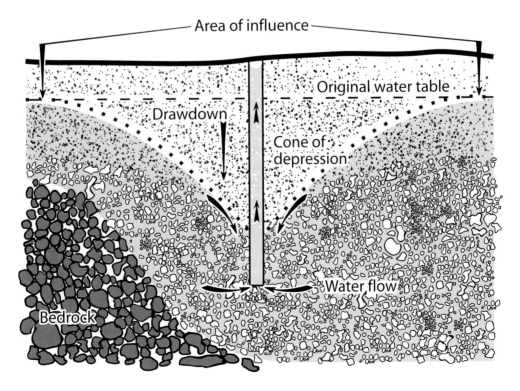

When water is pumped out of a well, water from surrounding areas flows toward the intake at the bottom of the well. If water could flow immediately through the aquifer, the water level at the top of the aquifer would immediately adjust to keep the top of the water table horizontal. However, since water must flow through the pores in an aquifer, the water table can develop a dip around the well, called a *cone of depression*, as shown in the picture above. The cone is deepest at the site of the well, but it may cover a large area. The depth of a cone of depression is called its *drawdown*. The depth and width of a cone of depression depends on the difference between the rate at which water is being drawn through the well and the rate at which water can pass through the aquifer.

*Saltwater intrusion* is the movement of saltwater from the sea into an overdrawn freshwater aquifer. This is a particular concern in coastal regions where saltwater from the sea can be absorbed by the ground. Such seawater does not usually mix with the freshwater in aquifers because the water table is usually higher than sea level and because less-dense freshwater floats above denser saltwater. However, when wells near the coast are overdrawing freshwater from an aquifer, the cone of depression can lower the water table below sea level, giving saltwater the opportunity to flow into the aquifer towards the wells. In extreme cases, so much saltwater can enter into an aquifer that it can no longer be used for drinking. Currently, saltwater intrusion threatens the quality of water in many communities that depend on wells along the Atlantic and Pacific coasts.

However, saltwater intrusion can be stopped by introducing artificial recharge, reducing pumping, or drilling relief wells that pump the saltwater out before it mixes with the groundwater. Drilling relief wells to keep the saltwater separated from the fresh groundwater can also reduce intrusion.

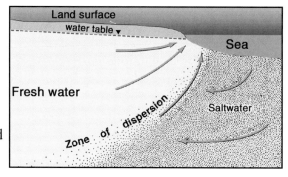

Sometimes when an aquifer is overdrawn, the land above the cone of depression begins to sink. This sinking is called *land subsidence*. It occurs when large amounts of groundwater have been withdrawn from certain types of sediments or rocks that compress when they lose water. These include sediments with fine grains like clay, limestone, carbonate rock, and salt beds. Fine-grained sediments compress because the water is partly responsible for holding up the ground. Even though this might seem impossible, underground water is actually a very strong supporter of the land that we walk on. When this groundwater is withdrawn through wells, the sediments become less stable and are compressed by the weight of the overlying sediments. The result is a slow but steady land subsidence. Sometimes, land subsidence is not easily observed because it takes place over decades. However, well pumping can lower large areas of land by tens of feet.

Subsidence in areas with groundwater withdrawal from limestone and other carbonate rocks typically occurs on smaller, but more serious scales. Land surfaces as small as a few square feet may suddenly collapse, causing what are called *sinkholes*. They can especially be a problem when they occur under a house or a highway. Sinkholes are common where the underground rocks (generally limestone) are dissolved by groundwater circulating through them. As the rocks dissolve, spaces are created between the underground rocks, into which the overlying land may collapse. Sinkholes appear suddenly because the land usually appears to be solid and stable for quite a while. Even though the problem may not be visible from the surface, underground spaces get too large. The remaining water will not support the land surface, and the ground collapses. Land subsidence is the result of a long process that begins deep underground, caused by the overuse of groundwater. It is very difficult to stop subsidence once it has started. However, scientific efforts can help predict it and monitor its development to ensure public safety.

The effects of groundwater over-pumping and declining water tables take place underground and out of sight. This can make them difficult for people to understand and take seriously. As land subsidence and saltwater intrusion occur more frequently, the consequences of aquifer drawdown become clearer. Wells are a way of life in many parts of the country, but overuse threatens the natural balance between groundwater recharge and withdrawal. Avoiding the problems of saltwater intrusion and land subsidence can only occur by maintaining this balance.

## Analysis Questions

1. In your own words, define and describe a cone of depression.

2. Why would saltwater intrusion be a danger to a city's water supply?

3. What is subsidence? Why is it such a difficult problem to remedy?

4. Answer the essential question: *Why should we be concerned about aquifer drawdown?*

## Lesson 4:
# Recharging and Balance

*Driving Question:* How does water get into aquifers?

## Overview

The last lesson outlined how people take water out of aquifers and what can happen if too much water is removed. In this lesson, you will look at where aquifer water comes from. Much of the water comes from the surface, the rest flows from other parts of the aquifer. No matter where the water comes from, there needs to be a balance between the water that enters an aquifer and the water that leaves it. When an imbalance occurs, as in Fresno, there are ways to restore the balance. As you read about the inputs and outputs to aquifers, think about how Fresno residents might change their behavior to maintain the water in their aquifer for future use.

## Important Content

- Aquifers can be large, and can cross watershed, county, and state boundaries.

- All the rain that falls within a watershed feeds the rivers, lakes and aquifers of that watershed.

# California Aquifers

 **Essential Question:** *Why is water movement in aquifers important?*

## Overview

California's largest and most used aquifers are in the Central Valley. In the Central Valley, the aquifer is mostly composed of sediment. This sediment has been accumulating for millions of years. The sediment that originally constructed the valley was deposited millions of years ago by the Pacific Ocean. In more recent geologic times, rivers and streams have deposited sediments by transporting large amounts of eroded materials from the mountain ranges surrounding the Central Valley. The most recent sediments make up the rich soil that supports an enormous farming industry and a large residential population.

To picture the sediments that make up the aquifer under the Central Valley, imagine the valley as a very deep, rock-lined basin between two mountain ranges running from north to south. Over periods of millions of years, that valley has been filled up with sediments to form the ground level that we see today.

You will see two diagrams of the aquifers in California on the following pages. The first is a map of aquifer boundaries representing what you might see if you could look down through the soil surface. The boundary of an aquifer is a location where there is a transition between different underground substances, such that the rate at which water flows on one side of the boundary is substantially different from that on the other. In some cases, impermeable layers can separate aquifers, but in others, the boundary is a border between aquifers made of different substances with different properties.

The second diagram is a cross-section of the Central Valley as viewed looking north from southern California. This diagram shows the solid rock of the mountain ranges and the layers of sediment that have been deposited in between them, over millions of years.

Use the two diagrams to answer the Analysis Questions.

## Analysis Questions

1. Look at the second picture – the cross-section of California. The Central Valley is located between which two mountain ranges?

2. If there were a source of pollution in the Sierra Nevada Mountains, would people living in the Great Central Valley need to be concerned? Why or why not?

3. Look at the first picture – the aquifers in California. Focus on the large aquifer in the center of California. Suppose farmers in northern California were using nitrogen fertilizers on their fields and letting the runoff seep into the aquifer. Should people in southern California be concerned about this?

4. Give evidence to support or oppose this statement: Since the Central Valley aquifers are like a big underground lake, any contamination will be diluted and we do not need to worry about it.

5. Answer the essential question: *Why is water movement in aquifers important?*

**Map of California Aquifers**

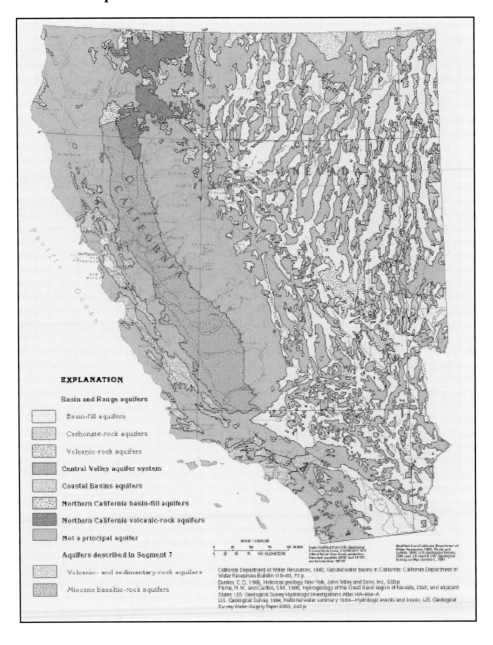

EXPLANATION

Basin and Range aquifers

Basin-fill aquifers

Carbonate-rock aquifers

Volcanic-rock aquifers

Central Valley aquifer system

Coastal Basins aquifers

Northern California basin-fill aquifers

Northern California volcanic-rock aquifers

Not a principal aquifer

Aquifers described in Segment 7

Volcanic- and sedimentary-rock aquifers

Miocene basaltic-rock aquifers

## A Cross-Section of the Central Valley in California

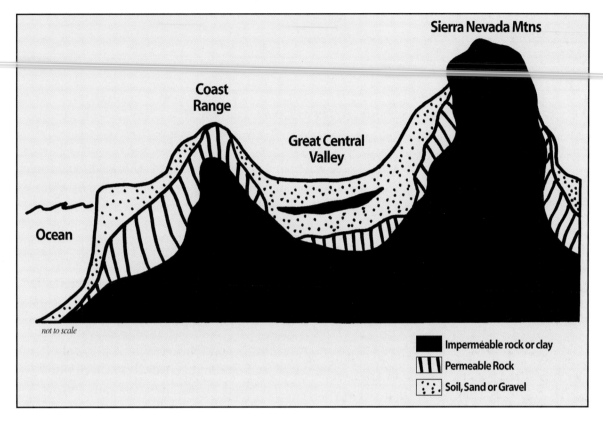

Sierra Nevada Mtns

Coast
Range

Great Central
Valley

Ocean

not to scale

■ Imperméable rock or clay

▥ Permeable Rock

⣿ Soil, Sand or Gravel

# Watersheds

**Essential Question:** *What is a watershed?*

## Procedure

Read the following article and answer the Analysis Questions.

## What is a Watershed?

A watershed is a region of land whose surface waters all drain into the same river or other body of water. As rain hits land or snow melts, water may be absorbed and filtered down through the layers of rock and soil to replenish aquifers. However, if the land is partially impermeable, or if it is too saturated to absorb any more water, then that water will remain on the surface, where gravity tries to pull it downhill.

Unless the water evaporates, or infiltrates into the soil, or reaches a pond or lake with no downhill path out, it will continue to travel downhill into progressively larger rivers and eventually into an ocean.

Because water flows from high to low elevations, the boundary of a watershed is determined by the elevation of the surrounding land. The highest points in the region mark the watershed boundary. In the image above, the dark black line represents the watershed boundary. It is the highest point of elevation separating the inner valley from the mountain ridges. Water flows down on both sides of the boundary into the river below.

One of the purposes of topographic maps is to show watersheds. You can identify watersheds on a topographic map by looking for two symbols. First, blue lines represent surface water. Second, brown lines represent lines of constant elevation, called contours. If you trace a contour line, you will be tracing a flat path. If you cross a contour, you will be tracing an uphill or downhill path. Since you know water flows downhill, you can outline a watershed by following the ridgelines connecting the highest elevations surrounding a lake or stream.

Patterns of landforms also determine how water flows. Where the slope is steep, water flows rapidly. Where the slope is gentle, water flows more slowly. If the sides of a river or stream are steep, then it will be narrow and deep. If the sides are shallow, it will be wider and shallower.

While all watersheds work the same way, they exist in all sizes. In fact, small watersheds flowing into streams are part of larger watersheds flowing into rivers. The watershed feeding a small river, in turn, is part of a larger watershed feeding into a larger river, and so on, until you reach a river that flows into an ocean. So, a watershed can be as small as a backyard that drains into a pond or as large as the California Regional Watershed that covers most of California, as well as parts of Oregon and Nevada. That watershed drains thousands of square miles to the Pacific Ocean. The Mississippi River watershed drains waters from 31 states! The California Regional Watershed has ten subregions of watersheds, and there are many more smaller watersheds inside of those.

No matter where you live or work, you are in a watershed. Each watershed has unique inter-related processes that determine its landscape, its water quality, and, in turn, your life. Any activity that affects the water quality, quantity, or rate of movement at one location can affect the watershed at locations downstream.

## Analysis Questions

1. What determines the boundary of a watershed?

2. To outline a watershed, what two symbols do you need to look at on a topographic map?

3. Answer the essential question: *What is a watershed?*

# Watersheds and Aquifers

 ***Essential Question:*** *How are watersheds related to aquifers?*

## Overview

Watersheds and aquifers are both part of the same water system. Watersheds are important because they store and transport water in streams, lakes, and rivers. Aquifers are important because they store and transport water through invisible underground terrain. Surface water throughout a watershed seeps through the soil to reach an aquifer below. How do we know which aquifer it will go into? In this lesson, you will identify aquifers lying under California watersheds.

## Procedure

Study the map of California watersheds on the next page and the map of California aquifers from Lesson 4: *California Aquifers.*

## Analysis Questions

1. Highlight the watersheds that appear to overlap with the Central Valley aquifer.

2. Which of these watersheds appear to overlap with more that one aquifer?

3. Answer the essential question: *How are watersheds related to aquifers?*

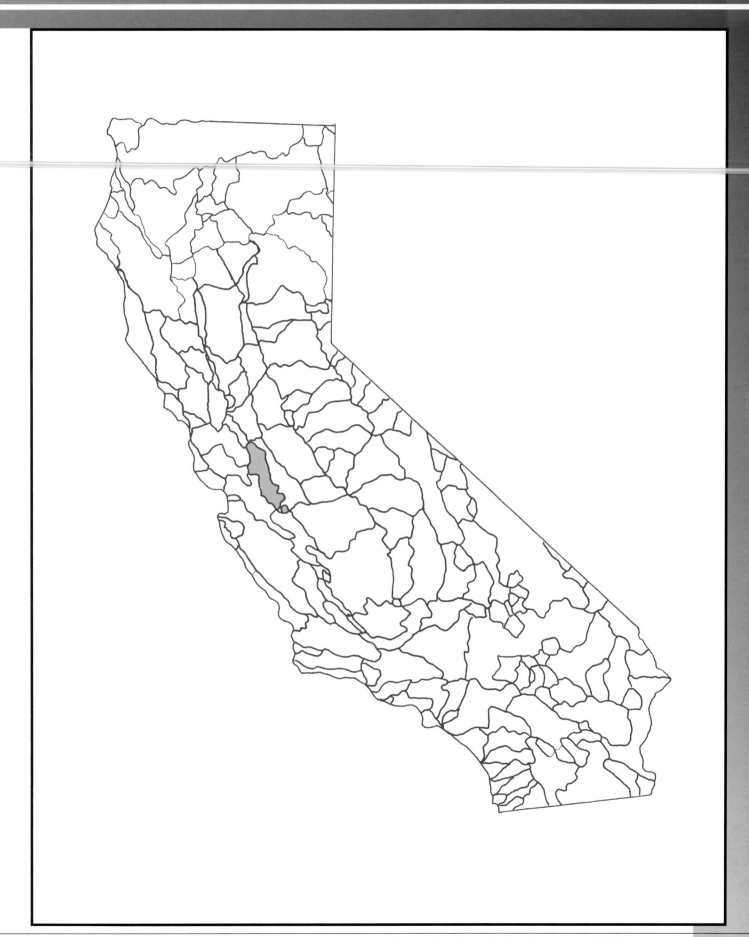

# Balance

 ***Essential Question:*** *Why does there need to be a balance in the water that enters and leaves a body of water?*

## Discussion

Consider the following questions:

1. Do you or someone you know have a checking account and a checkbook? What does it mean to balance your checkbook? Why is balancing your checkbook important?

2. What happens to your checkbook balance if you have more money coming in than going out? What happens if you have more money going out than coming in?

3. Think about this same principle in terms of water. Imagine a lake that provides the water supply for a town. How does water enter the lake? How does water leave the lake?

4. Which of the changes in the lake's water supply depend on natural phenomena? Which are more affected by human actions?

5. How would an expanding population in the town affect the water balance in the lake?

6. Can you take more water out of a lake than comes in? How could you do this? What would be the short-term effect of taking more water out than comes in? What would be the long-term effect? What would be the effect on water availability?

7. How would your answers to the previous questions be different for an aquifer rather than a lake?

8. Answer the essential question: *Why does there need to be a balance in the water that enters and leaves a body of water?*

# Aquifer Recharge

***Essential Question:*** *How do recharge basins help get water into an aquifer?*

## Overview

You have seen that there can be an imbalance between the amount of water that naturally enters an aquifer and the amount that is taken out. When this happens, the balance can be restored in several ways. One method is the use of *recharge basins*, which are shallow pools of water that are allowed to drain slowly into the aquifer. Recharge basins are inexpensive to construct and operate. Some basins are designed to fill with runoff that would otherwise drain into rivers and leave the watershed. Other recharge basins are filled by diverting water from rivers. Both basin types are used in many areas of the country, including Peoria, Illinois; Long Island, New York; Orange County, California; and Fresno, California.

The following is a list of frequently asked questions taken from a website about Leaky Acres, a recharge basin in Fresno. Read it and answer the Analysis Questions.

## Frequently Asked Questions about Leaky Acres

**What is the purpose of Leaky Acres?**

The Leaky Acres facility is currently comprised of 26 ponds covering 200 acres. It was built in 1970 to store water that is percolated, or drained, into the underground aquifer to recharge the groundwater supply.

**How much water is put into Leaky Acres?**

Over the past five years, it has received an average of 55 acre-feet per day. This is equivalent to approximately 18 million gallons.

**Can the recharge results be seen in the surrounding area?**

Yes, there is a big difference at a pump station located nearby. The water level at this location can rise as much as 10 feet when it is recharging. When recharging stops, it returns to its original level.

**How deep are the ponds?**

It varies, but the average depth is 3 to 3 1/2 feet.

**How long does water run into Leaky Acres?**

It runs nearly year-round.

**Are the soil conditions in Leaky Acres favorable for effective recharge?**

Yes; if more money was available and Leaky Acres could be deepened, it would be even more effective.

**Are there other recharge basins in Fresno?**

There are many others. The city has an agreement to use some of the Fresno Metropolitan Flood Control basins for the same purpose. However, it cannot use them year-round. Recharge operations usually begin in March and run until about October. The Fresno Metropolitan Flood Control District must keep its basins available for storm water during the rainy season to minimize the chances of local flooding.

**Are other recharge basins being planned?**

There are plans to develop a 40-acre facility. It will be located near the future water treatment plant at International and Maple in northeast Fresno.

**What sort of wildlife comes into the area?**

Pelicans, Canada geese, mallard ducks, American pintail ducks, and Chinese hornbill geese are among the waterfowl spotted at Leaky Acres. There are quite a few jackrabbits, and even a few red foxes and bobcats have been spotted in the last few years.

**Are there fish in the ponds?**

The Mosquito Abatement District stocks minnows to control mosquitoes. There are other fish that have managed to make it into Leaky Acres, but their numbers are few.

**Do kids swim or fish in Leaky Acres?**

Swimming and fishing are prohibited for safety reasons.

## Analysis Questions

1. What is the purpose of Leaky Acres? How big is it?

2. Can you think of a way (covered in a previous chapter) that water could be lost from Leaky Acres? How might this make surface recharge basins less effective?

3. What might be done to improve the amount of water recharged at Leaky Acres?

4. Answer the essential question: *How do recharge basins help get water into an aquifer?*

# Lesson 5:
# Pollution and Water Movement

 *Driving Question: How do pollutants move through water in an aquifer?*

## Overview

In the last lesson you learned how water moves in, out, and through aquifers and watersheds. In this lesson, we will look at how this water may carry pollution. Since water moves within an aquifer and watershed, if one source of water into the aquifer or watershed is polluted, all the water can become polluted. This can be an even greater problem if water moves from one aquifer or watershed to another. Pollution comes from many sources and occurs in many forms. For many years, people did not realize that aquifers were as interconnected as they are. In fact, it used to be common for people to dump old chemicals and trash down abandoned wells. We know that chemicals that enter the aquifer are often transported miles away by water. These contaminants can affect water quality for many years.

This lesson covers different types of groundwater pollution and looks at aquifer connections in California. In the next lesson, you will learn how to test water for salinity (salt content) and nitrates to determine if it is polluted.

## Important Content
*   Water seeps into aquifers from the surface. This seeping water can carry pollution with it.

# Diffusion Demonstrations

**Essential Question:** *Define diffusion in your own words.*

## Overview

Pollution moves through underground water through a process called diffusion. In this activity, you will do a simple experiment to observe this process.

## Materials

1 large glass beaker

water

eyedropper

food coloring

## Safety

Follow standard safety rules and school safety rules for laboratory activities.

## Procedure

1. Fill the beaker 3/4 full with water. Let the beaker and water sit still for a few minutes until all the waves and ripples have subsided.

2. Drop three drops of food coloring into the beaker. Do not stir. Record your observations.

3. Wait a few more minutes and record another observation.

## Analysis Question

1. The food coloring moved through the water by a process called diffusion. Answer the essential question: *Define diffusion in your own words.*

# Water Movement

 **Essential Question:** *What direction does water move underground?*

## Procedure

Take notes as your teacher demonstrates pollution movement on a groundwater model.

## Analysis Questions

1. How does point source pollution get into the groundwater?

2. Sketch what it looks like as it spreads.

3. How does non-point source pollution spread differently?

4. How is pollution movement related to diffusion?

5. Answer the essential question: *What direction does water move underground?*

# Lesson 6:
# Point and Non-point Source Pollution in Fresno

 **Driving Question:** *Is pollution a problem for the wells under Fresno?*

## Overview

You learned in the last lesson that Fresno sits on a large aquifer that lies under most of California's Central Valley. Drawing water from a large aquifer has both benefits and drawbacks. The large size holds more water, but it is also vulnerable to pollution from many places. In this lesson, you will test the water quality from several sample wells in Fresno. You will determine if and where contaminants have spread through the aquifer. Based on this information, you will select three locations near the city where new wells might be placed.

## Important Content

- Pollution can come from single point sources, or more general non-point sources.

- Some pollutants, like nitrates, can cause diseases if they are concentrated in the water we drink.

- Water quality testing is an important way of ensuring the safety of the water we drink.

# Point Source Pollution in Fresno

 **Essential Question:** *What areas of the aquifer under Fresno are at risk from point sources of pollution?*

## Overview

Read the following passage about the point sources of pollution affecting the aquifer beneath Fresno.

## Point Source Pollution in Fresno

Contaminants are particles and substances that make something impure. When contaminants in water, air, or food are harmful to living organisms, we call those contaminants pollution. Contaminants can enter groundwater from a variety of sources. One of the characteristics used to describe sources of pollution is whether it is from a single location (point source) or from a larger area (non-point source). Point sources of pollution include underground storage tanks for chemicals, gas stations, and old wells people have used for garbage disposal. If one of these potential sources of pollution were to leak into a water supply, it would enter the water and form what is known as a plume. In a plume, a substance spreads out from its source in the water.

The following paragraphs describe several point sources of pollution in the Fresno area.

In the west side of the city, just north of test well #18, there is a contamination plume of chloride ions. This pollution started in the 1950's when wastewater from an ice production facility was dumped in local pits. The plume is slowly spreading to the southwest and is currently about 3 miles long and 1 mile wide.

A trichloroethylene (TCE) plume exists in the northern part of the city. It starts just west of test well #6 and extends southwest past test well #5. The source of the TCE is several closed manufacturing plants. Several wells in the area have been closed because of contamination from this plume. This contamination continues to spread to the south and southwest.

A third plume of point source pollution begins at the Fresno Air Terminal. This plume begins near test well #21 and has extended as far as test well #23. The plume contains contamination from fuel storage, cleaning product disposal, and waste lubricants from airplanes. Wells in this area are carefully monitored to track the extent of the contamination.

The fourth point source of pollution is from gasoline storage facilities. Some of these are gas stations where the underground tanks are leaking. Because it is difficult to determine when an underground tank is leaking, it is hard to know the extent of the contamination. At several of these sites, contamination has been detected in the nearby groundwater. At other sites, nothing has been detected, but there is reason to believe that contamination may soon reach the aquifer. Five facilities are being monitored. They are located: (1) halfway between test well #13 and test well #17, (2) 0.5 miles northeast of test well #18, (3) 0.5 miles southeast of test well #24, (4) halfway between test well #22 and test well #25, and (5) 1 mile northwest of test well #26.

## Analysis Questions

1. Based on the reading above, make markings on the Fresno map to show the locations of the point sources of pollution.

2. Based on the direction the plumes of pollution are moving, how would you expect the plumes from the gasoline storage facilities to spread?

3. Answer the essential question: *What areas of the aquifer under Fresno are at risk from point sources of pollution?*

**Part of Fresno County with Fresno city limits (light gray lines)**—The circles represent all wells in the city; the squares are wells that have been tested for contamination.

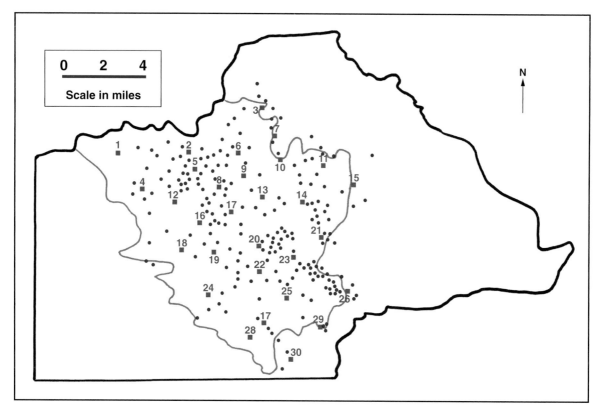

# Non-point Nitrogen Pollution

***Essential Question:*** *Which areas of the aquifer under Fresno have the highest nitrate concentrations? Which areas have the lowest?*

## Overview

Pollution also enters water from non-point sources. Non-point source pollution enters water from a more general area. Some examples of non-point pollution include: fertilizer and pesticide runoff from farms, oil and gasoline from streets, and salt used to melt ice on roads and sidewalks in cities. Non-point source pollution can be difficult to control because it is more difficult to identify the source of the problem.

In this activity, you will test for nitrate pollution, which often results from farm runoff or human sewage. In the aquifer beneath Fresno, several areas have been affected by nitrate pollution. In the next activity, you will read about the health risks of having nitrates in water supplies. It will help you understand why it is important to keep the water supply free of excessive nitrates.

## Materials

nitrate test kits

water samples from your teacher

## Safety

Follow standard safety rules and school safety rules for laboratory activities.

## Procedure

1. Follow your teacher's instructions for the samples you will test for nitrates.

2. For each sample assigned by your teacher, follow the instructions in your kit to measure the nitrate nitrogen.

3. Match the color of your sample to the color in the test kit. Record the value in a table.

4. For each sample you test, record your test results in a table.

5. Share your results with the class and record their results in your table.

## Analysis Questions

1. Based on your class results, devise a way to represent your results on the map. (Use color, symbols, or another system to indicate the nitrate concentration at each well.)

2. Answer the essential question: *Which areas of the aquifer under Fresno have the highest nitrate concentrations? Which areas have the lowest?*

**Test well sites in Fresno, California**

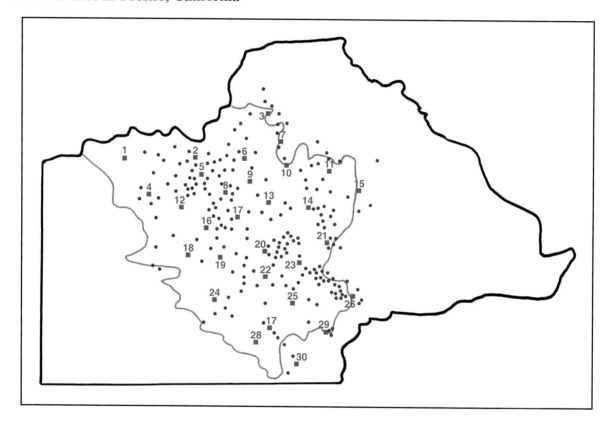

# Effects of Nitrate Pollution

 *Essential Question:* Why is it important to monitor pollutant levels in groundwater?

## Overview

Read the following article and answer the Analysis Questions that follow.

## Nitrates in Groundwater

Nitrates are chemicals that contain nitrogen. Even though nitrates are invisible, their overabundance in the air, soil, groundwater, and surface water can be harmful to human health. While large amounts are harmful to humans, nitrate ($NO_3$) and a similar compound known as nitrite ($NO_2$) are essential nutrients for plant and animal growth. One of the ways humans release nitrate into the environment is by applying fertilizer to lawns and crops. These nitrogen compounds are also found in animal and human waste. Waste from large-scale factory farms (where thousands of animals are raised in close quarters), city sewer systems, refuse dumps, animal feed lots, and septic systems raise levels of nitrate in our environment as well.

The quantity of these chemicals found in groundwater is usually a result of human activities in the upstream watershed or on the land above the aquifer. Nitrate and nitrite levels are generally highest in farming areas because nitrogen-rich chemicals are used to fertilize growing crops. In fact, the agriculture industry applies eleven million tons of nitrogen compounds in the form of chemical fertilizer every year. Another 6.5 million tons of nitrogen compounds are applied each year as manure. Nitrogen fertilizers dissolve in water and do not evaporate. This allows them to move easily through soil and into the drinking water supply.

Nitrate contamination of drinking water depends on two factors. The first is the amount of nitrogen being applied above ground. The other is the maintenance of the wells below the ground. Well pipes frequently have leaks in their first 20 feet underground. It is almost impossible to keep nitrate contamination out of these tiny holes in the pipe. Because nitrates move with the flow of groundwater, the chemical source may be located a considerable distance from the well, but a risk for water contamination still exists.

The Maximum Contaminant Level for nitrate ($NO_3$), enforced by the U.S. Environmental Protection Agency is 45 mg/L (millgrams/liter). In the safer areas of the U.S., the average amount of nitrates found in drinking water is about 4 mg (milligrams) for every 2 L (liters) of water consumed daily. In these conditions, nitrates comprise only a small portion of a usual daily intake of water. However, there have been places in the U.S. where daily intake of nitrates was found to be five times higher than the EPA's Maximum Contaminant Level. Prolonged intake of this amount of nitrates can be harmful or even fatal.

# The Health Effects of High Nitrate Concentrations

High nitrate concentrations may cause a disease known as "blue baby syndrome." It is a blood disorder that impairs an infant's blood's ability to carry oxygen throughout the body. Hemoglobin is the major carrier of oxygen to body cells. Stomach acids convert nitrates to nitrites. Nitrites get absorbed in the bloodstream and react with the hemoglobin in red blood cells preventing the blood from supplying enough oxygen to the body's cells and tissues. Babies are more likely to develop this disease because they have not developed protection from harmful nitrate/nitrite levels. Most cases of "blue baby syndrome" have been traced to babies' drinking milk formula mixed in water with high levels of nitrate contamination. The disease can result in brain damage and death.

Nitrates in groundwater can also be indicators of the potential for other contaminants to be present as well. Where fertilizers are being applied to fields, other agricultural chemicals, such as fungicides and herbicides are often used as well. The nitrates from the fertilizer along with these other chemicals can contaminate the groundwater. If the source of contamination is animal waste or septic tanks, disease-causing bacteria, viruses, and protozoa may also be present in the water.

In surface waters like ponds, streams, and reservoirs, nitrates are important to plants for photosynthesis and growth. However, too much nitrogen in water can cause a rapid growth of plants and algae. When these plants and algae die, their decomposition can remove so much of the oxygen from the water that fish and other aquatic organisms suffocate and die. This process is called eutrophication.

## Prevention and Correction

Infants or individuals with health problems should not consume drinking water containing more nitrates than the Maximum Contaminant Level allows. Bottled water or water taken from another safe source should be used instead. Simple water filters do not remove nitrates. Expensive techniques like ionization, reverse osmosis, or distillation can be effective. However, these treatment systems are expensive and require careful maintenance. In some cases, drilling a deeper well into non-contaminated water may be the least expensive solution.

## Analysis Questions

1. What part of the body does nitrate poisoning affect?

2. Suppose a case of "blue baby syndrome" was discovered in a community that gets drinking water from underground. How could you find the source of the pollution?

3. What is eutrophication? What causes it? How does it affect ecosystems in surface waters like ponds, streams, and reservoirs?

4. The EPA has set standards for "acceptable" levels of nitrates in drinking water. It also has standards for "acceptable" levels of pesticides and other toxic chemicals. Write a paragraph presenting your opinion about whether or not you agree that there is such a thing as an acceptable level of nitrates or other chemicals in people's drinking water.

5. Think about what you have learned about groundwater and aquifers. Why do you think it is nearly impossible for pollutants to be removed once they have entered an aquifer?

6. Answer the essential question: *Why is it important to monitor pollutant levels in groundwater?*

# Total Dissolved Solids

 ***Essential Question:*** *Which areas of the aquifer under Fresno have the highest levels of total dissolved solids? Which areas have the lowest levels?*

## Overview

The mineral and salt in water, together with small quantities of organic matter, are called total dissolved solids. Dissolved solids are not harmful, but they can affect the taste, odor, and color of water, which affect how it can be used. For example, if water contains too much salt, people will object to the taste, or if it is discolored, it cannot be used for laundry. Water with large amounts of total dissolved solids will often need to be treated before it can be used. High levels of dissolved solids in water may be an indication that an aquifer is being overdrawn.

One way of testing for dissolved solids in water is by measuring the electrical conductivity of the water. While this test does not measure all the forms of dissolved solids, it is a reliable measure of the amount of salt in the water. Electrical conductivity tests how well electricity passes through water. The more ions from salt occur in water, the higher the water's electrical conductivity will be. In this activity, you will measure the conductivity of the water from several Fresno wells to determine the amount of salt in the water.

## Procedure

1. Follow your teacher's instructions for the samples you will test for total dissolved solids.

2. For each sample assigned by your teacher, follow the instructions in your kit to measure the electrical conductivity.

3. Match the measurement of electrical conductivity to the corresponding value for total dissolved solids.

4. For each sample you test, record your results in a table.

5. Share your results with the class and add their results to your table.

## Safety

Follow standard safety rules and school safety rules for laboratory activities.

## Analysis Questions

1. Collect all of your class data in one table. Which location had the highest electrical conductivity? Which had the lowest?

2. Based on your class results, come up with a way to show your results on the map below. (Use color, symbols, or another way to indicate the total dissolved solids at each well.)

3. Answer the essential question: *Which areas of the aquifer under Fresno have the highest levels of total dissolved solids? Which areas have the lowest levels?*

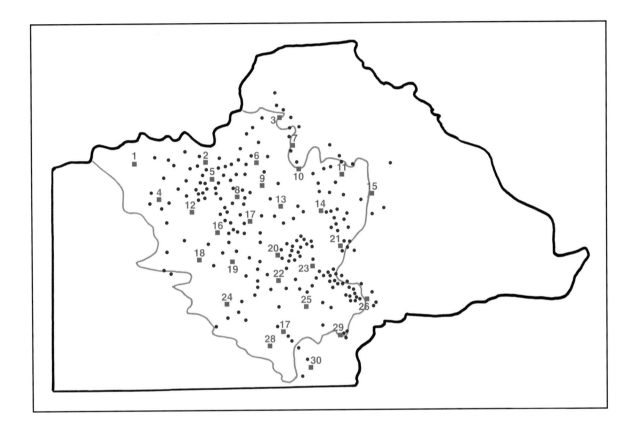

# Well Sites

 ***Essential Question:*** *What is the best location for a new well? Why is it at the least risk for contamination from point and non-point source pollution?*

## Overview

Based on the information from the last two activities, you will select three locations for new wells in Fresno, based on pollution. When they choose locations for wells, engineers consider many other factors, but for your decision today, you will consider only the point and non-point sources of pollution in Fresno's aquifer.

## Analysis Questions

1. Look at the two maps you developed in the last two lessons. Based on those maps, what locations would be the best places to dig new wells for the city of Fresno? Remember that the wells must be within the city limits (the light gray lines).

2. Answer the essential question: *What is the best location for a new well? Why is it at the least risk for contamination from point and non-point source pollution?*

# Lesson 7:
# A Plan for Fresno

 ***Driving Question:*** *What are the details of Fresno's aquifer problem?*

## Overview

So far, you have learned about Fresno's aquifer problem in general terms. In this lesson, you will look at the details of the situation. You will study the estimates for incoming and outgoing water flows and the amount of water that is withdrawn for different purposes. Fresno's city planners have a plan to manage the problem for the next several years. In this lesson, you will see the details of that plan. You will think about its implications and decide if you think it is the best idea for the city. This information will help you in the next chapter where you will consider all the parts of the Fresno water problem and come up with your own solution.

## Important Content

- In many places, water is taken out of aquifers faster than it can be replaced.

- Aquifers must be carefully managed to balance water inputs and outputs.

**Aquifers**

# Fresno Statistics

**Essential Question:** *What changes will Fresno have to make to comply with the Water Board's plan?*

## Overview

In 1992, the Fresno Water Board developed a plan for managing the amount of aquifer water until 2050. Managing the aquifer water includes managing surface water, since the two are closely connected. The chart below is taken from the report and shows inputs and outputs to the aquifer. The inflow and outflow volumes for 1992 are what actually happened. All other numbers are predictions.

## Procedure

Use the table below to answer the Analysis Questions.

## Analysis Questions

1. Complete the last column in the chart by calculating how much each inflow or outflow will change from 1992 to 2050. Use negative numbers to show a decrease and positive numbers to show an increase.

2. Which input variable changes the most? Which changes the least?

3. Suppose there are 450 acres of recharge ponds in 1992 and they recharge 56,718,000 m$^3$ of water. How many acres will be needed in 2050 to meet the need for 209,610,000 m$^3$ of water?

4. Which two output variables change the most?

5. The population of Fresno was 500,000 in 1992. How many people will Fresno be able to supply with water in 2050? Assume each person continues to use the same amount of water.

6. What percent population growth is this?

7. Notice that agricultural pumping is predicted to continue to decrease during this period (1992--2050). Assume that each acre of farmland continues to use the same amount of water. If there were 111,095 acres of irrigated farmland in 1992, how many acres will there be in 2050?

8. Answer the essential question: *What changes will Fresno have to make to comply with the Water Board's plan?*

    (Base your answer only on data in the table and your answers to the other Analysis Questions).

## Inputs and Outputs to the Fresno Aquifer

*(All units are m³ of water per year)*

| | | 1992 (actual) | 1997 (estimated) | 2010 (estimated) | 2050 (estimated) | Change from 1992 to 2050 |
|---|---|---|---|---|---|---|
| | Groundwater Inflow | 43,155,000 | 45,621,000 | 51,786,000 | 65,349,000 | |
| | Urban Intentional Recharge (recharge basins) | 56,718,000 | 65,349,000 | 91,242,000 | 209,610,000 | |
| | Other Recharge | 270,027,000 | 268,794,000 | 278,658,000 | 261,396,000 | |
| **Total Input Volume** | | **369,900,000** | **379,764,000** | **421,686,000** | **536,355,000** | |
| | Groundwater Outflow | 59,184,000 | 69,048,000 | 81,378,000 | 81,378,000 | |
| | Municipal Pumping | 150,426,000 | 172,620,000 | 215,775,000 | 368,667,000 | |
| | Misc. Pumping | 18,495,000 | 22,194,000 | 22,194,000 | 23,427,000 | |
| | Agricultural Pumping | 130,698,000 | 93,708,000 | 80,145,000 | 40,689,000 | |
| | Rural Residential Pumping | 20,961,000 | 22,194,000 | 22,194,000 | 22,194,000 | |
| **Total Output Volume** | | **379,764,000** | **379,764,000** | **421,686,000** | **536,355,000** | |
| Annual change in volume of water stored in the aquifer | | **-9,864,000** | **0** | **0** | **0** | |

*Groundwater inflow* is the amount of groundwater moving into the area from other parts of the aquifer.

*Urban Intentional Recharge* is another name for using recharge basins, which you read about in Lesson 4: *Recharging Reading.*

*Other Recharge* includes all natural recharge.

*Groundwater outflow* is the amount of groundwater moving away from the area into other parts of the aquifer.

*Municipal pumping* is water pumped out of the aquifer through wells for residential use.

*Miscellaneous pumping* is used for reasons other than municipal and agriculture.

*Rural residential pumping* is water pumped by rural residents, who often have wells on their own property.

# Evaluating the Plan

*Essential Question:* What other water supply alternatives are available for Fresno?

## Overview

In the last activity, you saw the plan the Fresno Water Board proposed for managing the Fresno aquifer until the year 2050. Now that you have calculated the important numbers, think about other alternatives available to the Fresno community. Use the information from Lesson 4: *Balance* and your knowledge of water use and aquifers to answer the Analysis Questions.

## Analysis Questions

1. Which variables in the chart from Lesson 7: *Fresno Statistics* can the citizens and government of Fresno change? How?

2. You calculated the number of people that Fresno will be able to support in 2050. Is there any way they could support more people? How?

3. Supporting more people in Fresno requires more water and that water must be pumped through wells. Based on what you learned about pollution plumes in groundwater, do you think there might be good locations for additional wells in Fresno? Why or why not?

4. You calculated the amount of farmland that can be irrigated in 2050. Is there any way more farmland could be irrigated?

5. What is your first impression of this plan? What parts do you think are good? What parts need to be improved?

6. Answer the essential question: *What other water supply alternatives are available for Fresno?*

# Water Management

# Chapter 6
# Water Management

## Connections

In this chapter, you will apply everything you have learned so far in the unit. This chapter asks you to combine your knowledge of soils, farming, dams, salmon, and aquifers. You will have to use all that knowledge to select a plan to help the people in Fresno meet their water needs for the next 50 years. While you make this decision, keep in mind that the population in the area is growing and will continue to grow. This presents a problem on both sides of the conflict. More residents means that more water will be used in Fresno. At the same time, populations are growing across the country. That increases the demand for food, which increases the need for farm products and irrigation water. Balancing these two needs is not easy, but that is your goal in this chapter.

## In this chapter:

You will start the chapter with some class discussions and overviews of "the big picture." This will help you bring together what you have learned throughout the unit. You will then see three proposals that have been suggested as solutions to Fresno's water shortage. You will use ArcView to gather information about Fresno. You will also read about some of the proposals' social implications. In the final lesson, you will use the Environmental Decision Making process to select the best proposal. Your decision will balance the consequences, the needs of the stakeholders, and your own constraints and considerations.

## When you're done you'll be able to:

- Evaluate possible solutions to the water shortage in Fresno.

- Balance the needs of stakeholders and consequences in a difficult decision.

- Use dams and recharge basins as tools to solve an environmental problem.

# Lesson 1
# System Out of Balance

 ***Driving Question:*** *How do all of the parts of the water problem fit together?*

## Overview

This lesson briefly summarizes what you have learned so far in this unit. So far, you have looked at dams, aquifers, and agriculture as separate ideas, but they are interconnected. Water from aquifers is pulled through wells into residents' kitchens. It is also pumped for irrigation on farms. Water in the reservoirs behind dams seeps into aquifers. There are many other connections and understanding them will help you decide how to make Fresno's water last another 50 years. Think about what you have learned as you prepare to make a decision on a solution to Fresno's water problem.

## Important Content

- The choice of irrigation system can make a big difference in the amount of water used on a farm.

- Dams provide water storage from rivers and streams. They do not create extra water, but hold back the flow of the river to regulate the river's flow, and to make more water available to people in times when the river is historically lower.

- In many places, water is taken out of aquifers faster than it can be replaced. This can cause sinkholes, land subsidence, saltwater intrusion, and increased salinity of water.

# Water as a System

**Essential Question:** *How are aquifers, dams, rainfall, and water use connected?*

## Overview

In past lessons, you determined how much water you could get from an additional dam and how much water is available in an aquifer. You also studied how much water people use daily and how much water farmers use on crops. Today, you will look at how all of these things fit together. You will see their connection by creating a diagram showing the water system around Fresno.

## Materials

poster-board and colored pencils or markers

## Procedure

In this lesson, you will create a diagram. It will show the portions of the global water cycle that you have studied so far in this unit.

1. Make a list of the sources of water for the Fresno area, such as rainfall and so on.

2. Make a list of where the water around Fresno goes, such as into the aquifer and downstream.

3. Create a diagram illustrating the different paths water can take as it moves through Fresno's water system. Use your knowledge of farming, dams, rivers, aquifers, and human water use. Your diagram should include items such as aquifers, rivers, recharge ponds, dams, rainfall, farms, and cities (human water use).

4. Try to think of all the possible ways that water could move from one section of the diagram to another. Remember to use arrows to indicate the direction the water is moving.

## Analysis Questions

1. List the ways that water could get into the aquifer in the Fresno region.

2. How could fresh water be supplied to farms and cities in and around Fresno?

3. How does evaporation affect each of the parts of the water system around Fresno?

4. Identify three places in your diagram where you think the system could use water more effectively. Describe how this might happen.

5. Do dams and reservoirs add water to the system? Explain your thinking.

6. Answer the essential question by writing a description of the diagram you drew. *How are aquifers, dams, rainfall, and water use connected?*

# Three Proposals

***Essential Question:*** *What should one consider when voting for a proposal?*

## Overview

In the next several lessons, you will take on the role of a citizen of Fresno. You will vote on a referendum to choose one of three possible plans to manage the area's water. Remember that there are many needs that must be met. The needs of the farmers, the residents, and the environment must all be considered carefully before you decide which plan deserves your vote. The proposal you vote for should be the one that you determine will provide the best possible solution to Fresno's water problem. Be prepared to defend your decision with evidence.

## Procedure

Read the referendum on the next page and answer the Analysis Questions.

## Analysis Questions

1. Three interested groups are listed below. Write one paragraph for each, describing their initial reaction to each proposal.

   a. farmers

   b. Fresno residents

   c. naturalists

2. Answer the essential question: *What should one consider when voting for a proposal?* For each proposal, write at least two questions you would like answered to help you make your decision.

# Official Ballot
### Proposition 4747

Check the appropriate box to indicate your vote. On the issue of creating a water budget up to the year 2050 for the counties of Fresno and Kings, in the State of California, the following three (3) plans are proposed:

## ❑ Proposal A

The borders of the City of Fresno will be permanently frozen. In order to maintain urban population as close to 750,000 persons as possible, the city limits shall not be expanded beyond their current boundaries.

The number of recharge basins in the area will continue to increase in accordance with the plan outlined in the Fresno Water Budget. (See Chapter 5, Lesson 7: *Fresno Statistics.*)

All farmers will be henceforth required by law to use irrigation systems that are at least 85% efficient.

## ❑ Proposal B

1000 km$^2$ of land currently reserved for grazing will be opened for farming.

All farmers will be henceforth required by law to use irrigation systems that are at least 85% efficient.

Consumers of water in urban areas will decrease their water use to 225 m$^3$ per person, per year.

Recognizing estimates that the urban population will reach 1,500,000 persons by the year 2050, the City of Fresno may annex new land. However, the City shall be prohibited from annexing more than 750 m$^3$ of new land between now and 2050. Furthermore, all new land annexed by the City must be land that is currently designated as grazing land.

A dam shall be built to support future urban population growth. (The site of the new dam will be chosen from the proposed locations identified in Chapter 3, Lesson 6: *Fresno Water Board.*)

After the above changes are enacted, any remaining water deficit will be rectified by purchasing water from other areas of the country, probably the central or northwest states.

## ❑ Proposal C

All farmers will be henceforth required by law to use irrigation systems that are at least 90% efficient.

Appropriate crops shall be chosen such that average evapotranspiration shall not exceed 539,470 m$^3$ per km$^2$ of farmland.

770 km$^2$ of farmland will be converted to wetlands.

In order to maintain the urban population as close to 1,000,000 persons as possible, the City of Fresno shall be prohibited from annexing more than 125 km$^2$ of land between now and the year 2050. Furthermore, all new land annexed by the City must be land that is currently designated as grazing land.

Consumers of water in urban areas will decrease their water use to 225 m$^3$ per person, per year.

# Group Constraints and Considerations

 **Essential Question:** *What made some considerations more important than others?*

## Overview

When environmental decisions need to be made, there are often groups of people with very different ideas about how to solve the problem. In this project, you will need to work with a group to make a decision you can all agree on. Your task today is to agree on a list of constraints and considerations to guide your group through the rest of the project. It is important to agree on your goals now, before you continue with the Environmental Decision Making Process in later lessons.

## Materials

proposals from Lesson 6: *Three Proposals*

## Procedure

Work with a group. Your group must reach agreement on a list of constraints and considerations. You will use this list to make your decision about which proposal to support. Remember that constraints are goals that you must reach or rules that you must not violate. Considerations are goals that you would like to achieve, but are not absolutely necessary.

Create a list of constraints and considerations with your group. Then use the Analysis Questions below to revise your lists.

## Analysis Questions

1. What are the absolute constraints your group agrees should not be violated in this decision?

2. What are the considerations you would like to achieve?

3. Rank your considerations from most to least important.

4. Answer the essential question with at least two paragraphs justifying your ranking. *What made some considerations more important than others?*

# Current State

***Essential Question:*** *Describe the current state of water use in the Fresno region.*

## Overview

You need to determine which of the three proposals on the referendum is the best solution for Fresno. As you gather data on the proposals, think about what each proposal would mean to people living in the area.

In this activity, you will use ArcView software to explore the current state of water use in the Fresno region.

## Materials

ArcView 3.2 installed on a Windows computer

**Fresno Water Management data file**
File name: final_project.apr
File type: ArcView Project

## Procedure

1. Open the Fresno Water Management ArcView project according to your teacher's instructions.

2. Using ArcView, determine the total area occupied by each category of land use. Copy your results to Water Use Table 1.

3. Use what you know about water use to calculate the total amount of water consumed by each land use category. (Some of the values in the chart have already been filled in for you.) You might find the information you learned in Chapter 5, Lesson 7: *Fresno Statistics* to be helpful.

4. Complete the tables on the next page.

## Analysis Question

1. Answer the essential question: *Describe the current state of water use in the Fresno region.*

## Procedure 1: The Current Situation

Here are some important facts you should consider.

- Currently, the average evapotranspiration in the area is 719,293 m³/km² (meters cubed per kilometer squared of farmland). Average irrigation efficiency is 78%.
- The average urban resident in Fresno today uses 300 m³ of water each year.

### Water Use Table 1 • Current State

|  | Area of Land Used (km²) | | Water Consumed (m³) |
|---|---|---|---|
| Prime Farmland |  | |  |
| Other Farmland |  | |  |
| Grazing Land |  | | 0 |
| Urban Land | Area: | Population: 500,000 |  |
| Water | 44 | | 0 |
|  |  | |  |
| **TOTAL** | **8202** | |  |

### Water Available Table 1 • Current State

|  | Volume Available (m³) |
|---|---|
| Water Available from the Aquifer |  |
| Water Available from Dams | 3,911,076,000 m³ |
| TOTAL |  |

# Proposal Analysis

 *Essential Question: How much water does each plan actually save?*

## Overview

In this activity, you will use ArcView to evaluate each of the referendum proposals and determine which of the three is the best solution for Fresno.

## Materials

 ArcView 3.2 installed on a Windows computer

**Fresno Water Management data file**
File name: final_project.apr
File type: ArcView Project

## Procedure

1. Open the Fresno Water management ArcView project according to your teacher's instructions.

2. Use ArcView to make the suggested changes in each of the three proposals described in Lesson 2: *Three Proposals*. For each proposal, complete the related data tables. If necessary, review other projects completed in this unit to find data about dams, aquifers and farming practices. Show your calculations or explain where you found the numbers you use.

## Analysis Question

1. Answer the essential question: *How much water does each plan actually save?*

# The Situation Under Proposal A

Here are some important facts to consider as you evaluate Proposal A.

- Currently, the available water from dams is 3,911,076,000 m$^3$. If you need to add a dam, find information about how much water will be made available. Review Chapter 3, Lesson 6: *Fresno Water Board* and Chapter 3, Lesson 6: *Data About Dams* if you need help.
- The average evapotranspiration in the area is 719,293 m$^3$/km$^2$ (meters cubed per kilometer squared of farmland). Average irrigation efficiency is 78%.
- The average urban resident in Fresno today uses 300 m$^3$ of water each year.

## Water Use Table A

Modify the ArcView project to determine the total area that would be occupied by each category of land use under Proposal A. Use what you know about water use to calculate the total amount of water consumed by each category of land users. (Some of the values in the chart have already been filled in for you.)

| | Area of Land Used (km$^2$) | | Water Consumed (m$^3$) |
|---|---|---|---|
| Prime Farmland | | | |
| Other Farmland | | | |
| Grazing Land | | | 0 |
| Urban Land | Area: | Population: | |
| Water | 44 | | 0 |
| | | | |
| **TOTAL** | **8202** | | |

## Water Available Table A

| | Volume Available (m$^3$) |
|---|---|
| Water Available from the Aquifer | |
| Water Available from Dams | |
| **TOTAL** | |

# The Situation Under Proposal B

Here are some important facts to consider as you evaluate Proposal B.

- Currently, the available water from dams is 3,911,076,000 m³. If you need to add a dam, find information about how much water will be made available. Review Chapter 3, Lesson 6: *Fresno Water Board* and Chapter 3, Lesson 6: *Data About Dams* if you need help.

- The average evapotranspiration in the area is 719,293 m³/km² (meters cubed per kilometer squared of farmland). Average irrigation efficiency is 78%.

- The average urban resident in Fresno today uses 300 m³ of water each year.

## Water Use Table B

Modify the ArcView project to determine the total area that would be occupied by each category of land use under Proposal B. Use what you know about water use to calculate the total amount of water consumed by each category of land users. (Some of the values in the chart have already been filled in for you.)

| | Area of Land Used (km²) | | Water Consumed (m³) |
|---|---|---|---|
| Prime Farmland | | | |
| Other Farmland | | | |
| Grazing Land | | | 0 |
| Urban Land | Area: | Population: | |
| Water | 44 | | 0 |
| Wetland | | | |
| | | | |
| TOTAL | 8202 | | |

## Water Available Table B

| | Volume Available (m³) |
|---|---|
| Water Available from the Aquifer | |
| Water Available from Dams | |
| TOTAL | |

# The Situation Under Proposal C

Here are some important facts to consider as you evaluate Proposal C.

- Currently, the available water from dams is 3,911,076,000 m³. If you need to add a dam, find information about how much water will be made available. Review Chapter 3, Lesson 6: *Fresno Water Board* and Chapter 3, Lesson 6: *Data About Dams* if you need help.
- The average evapotranspiration in the area is 719,293 m³/km² (meters cubed per kilometer squared of farmland). Average irrigation efficiency is 78%.
- The average urban resident in Fresno today uses 300 m³ of water each year.

## Water Use Table C

Modify the ArcView project to determine the total area that would be occupied by each category of land use under Proposal C. Use what you know about water use to calculate the total amount water consumed by each category of land users. (Some of the values in the chart have already been filled in for you.)

| | Area of Land Used (km²) | | Water Consumed (m³) |
|---|---|---|---|
| Prime Farmland | | | |
| Other Farmland | | | |
| Grazing Land | | | 0 |
| Urban Land | Area: | Population: | |
| Water | 44 | | 0 |
| | | | |
| TOTAL | 8202 | | |

## Water Available Table C

| | Volume Available (m³) |
|---|---|
| Water Available from the Aquifer | |
| Water Available from Dams | |
| TOTAL | |

# Lesson 3
# Social and Political Concerns

**?** *Driving Question:* What are the social and political consequences of the proposals?

## Overview

In the last lesson, you gathered information about the three proposed solutions to Fresno's water problem. However, the information you gathered did not cover the whole story. Your calculations showed how much water would be used and how much would be returned to the aquifer. You have not yet considered the social and political consequences of each proposal. For example, what happens to a city when you restrict urban growth? Does that make the city a better or worse place to live? In this lesson, you will learn more about these social and political issues. This information will help you understand the consequences of your decision. It will also help you see how different stakeholders might be affected by changes in water policy.

## Important Content

* Our nation is dependent on California produce, and water management decisions will have an impact on its availability throughout the nation and the world.

* Restricting the growth of urban areas has both positive and negative consequences.

* Environmental changes due to water management policies can be both positive and negative.

# Harry Winter Again

**Essential Question:** *What social and political factors will be affected by your water management decision?*

## Procedure

Look back at Chapter 1, Lesson 1: *The Harry Winter Show*. Re-read the transcript of the show and answer the following questions.

## Analysis Questions

1. List all of the social or political concerns people in the show have about the current use of water in Fresno.

2. Which of these issues are addressed by proposal A? Which are addressed by proposal B? Which are addressed by proposal C?

3. What do you think will happen if a proposal is selected that does not address all of the concerns raised by the guests on the Harry Winter Show?

4. Knowing what you now know about water use, can you think of any issues that concern the current situation that were not raised on the show?

5. Answer the essential question: *What social and political factors will be affected by your water management decision?*

# Controlling Urban Population

 *Essential Question:* How does the issue of increasing urban population affect your decision on the water management proposals?

## Overview
Read the following passage and answer the Analysis Questions.

## Controlling Urban Population

What happens when a population becomes too big for a community to support? How does the community use its resources? Where do all the people go? One response to these questions is urban sprawl. Urban sprawl is the spread of development beyond a city onto rural land. In other words, when a city gets too crowded, or its resources become limited, people start moving out of the city and start building homes and living in the surrounding areas of the city. Sometimes with urban sprawl, the population of the city and surrounding areas have not grown at all, but the population of people have spread out over more land. The result is more land used per person. Often, urban sprawl means building over wetlands and woodlands. It can also mean building on farmland. Urban sprawl has sparked a national debate over land use. Some people think it threatens farmland and open space and harms the environment. Other people think it is a sign of growth and prosperity.

In California, almost all of the urban sprawl is the result of population growth. Even with sprawl, the number of people per square kilometer has grown consistently in recent decades. What would happen if the size of Fresno expanded as a result of population? For starters, there would be less farmland. Less farmland would mean that farmers would grow less produce, and there would be fewer farming jobs. If farmers grow less produce, then supermarket prices for produce would probably go up because the produce would need to be grown elsewhere. In addition to losing farmland, wetlands, woodlands, and other ecosystems would also be converted to human use if Fresno's urban area were to grow.

There are ways to limit urban sprawl. At least 19 states have either passed growth-management laws or set up task forces to protect farmland and open space. Dozens of cities and counties have established urban growth boundaries. Their aim is to limit development and stop the spread of urbanization to rural areas.

Portland, Oregon is one example of a city with growth boundaries. Developers there have to fill vacant lots inside the boundaries before the boundary lines will be moved. From the air, Portland's boundary is very obvious. Sprawling developments suddenly end, and miles of rural land begin. While the Portland area population has increased 25% in two decades, its developed land has increased only 2%.

Oregon farmers have benefited from this land-control policy. The Portland-area farm economy makes $500 million each year. Much of the state's top agricultural market is grown in the

Portland area. Without limits on urban sprawl, farmers would have lost a lot of land to urban development.

There are benefits inside the boundary as well. Developers have turned empty warehouses into apartments and stores. Old Portland neighborhoods have been rebuilt with new shops and galleries. This process of using existing areas in the city has saved tax money by not having to build roads into sprawling suburbs.

There is, however, another side to this issue. In the 1990s, Portland went through a huge economic boom. They had to find room for 15,000 newcomers a year inside its fixed boundaries. Traffic congestion became a problem. New single-family lots became half the size they were 20 years ago. The new constraints pushed land prices up 400% in seven years. In fact, home ownership decreased in Portland at a time when it was increasing throughout the rest of the country. The number of low-income apartments in downtown Portland also dropped 33% in five years. This caused the homeless rate to increase. Property had become so expensive that many people could no longer afford to live there.

Currently, the population in California is growing. A plan such as the one used in Portland would mean less space per person in already crowded areas. The transportation demands of more people create more traffic congestion. It would also mean more students per classroom in schools. Since undeveloped land in the city boundaries would have to be used before sprawling outward, there would be less room for parks and open areas. There would also be more apartment complexes and fewer large homes. Land price increases would result in higher rents and home values. The increased competition and demand for resources could create higher utility bills. That means residents would get less space for their money and have less money for luxury items. However, this kind of plan would also preserve farms and local ecosystems.

## Analysis Questions

1. What are some of the benefits of city boundaries and/or population restrictions?

2. What are some of the drawbacks of restricting urban, suburban, and/or population growth?

3. How is Portland's situation similar to and different from Fresno's?

4. Answer the essential question: *How does the issue of increasing urban population affect your decision on the water management proposals?*

# Buying and Selling Water

***Essential Question:*** *How does water marketing affect your decision about the water management proposals?*

## Overview

In this article you will read about some of the ways communities obtain water. As you read, think about where the water comes from, who has a right to the water, and what kind of impact water use has on the environment. Then answer the Analysis Questions.

## Buying and Selling Water

Can you put a price on water? What happens when there is not enough water in an area to meet the needs of the local population? Many regions of the U.S. currently have a growing need for fresh water and not enough water to meet their needs. Sometimes, this need is met through a practice called water marketing. Water marketing is the sale, exchange, or lease of water by one user to another. Water is not evenly distributed across the country. Therefore, some communities, such as the Great Lakes region, have large water resources, and other communities do not. Water marketing could become a way to meet the rising water demands for areas with limited water resources across the nation and the world.

A water shortage in El Paso, Texas provides some insight into the issues created by water marketing. The Hueco Bolson aquifer below El Paso has been used as a source of water for many years. Now the aquifer's supply is dwindling. Geologists say that by 2025, El Paso's growing population of 560,000 will have doubled and used up all the water stored in the aquifer. The shortage has led residents to consider importing water from Dell City, a nearby farming town of 50,000. The plan, however, could have harmful consequences. Dell City farmers would have to give up nearly half the water they use on their crops. This means they would not be able to plant and harvest as much. They would produce less food and make less money. They would also lose fertile lands as a result. That means there would not be as much land to farm on.

The plan also has potential benefits for Dell City residents. The aquifer under Dell City is a rich source of water. It is kept supplied by mountain streams in the northwest part of Texas. That means the aquifer naturally refills as long as water usage does not exceed a certain amount. Piping the water to El Paso would take care of 20% of that city's annual water needs. Another benefit for some Dell City residents is that while all surface water is public, groundwater is private in Texas. That means individuals could sell groundwater on their property. For example, a farmer in Dell City with 1,000 acres of land could make $200,000 a year selling the water under his land. However, this also raises a number of questions. Who set the prices for the water? How does El Paso decide whom they buy from? Can one landowner sell water under his property if it impacts his neighbor's farming productivity?

Since El Paso is still trying to solve their water shortage, it is helpful to see how water marketing has worked in the past. In fact, California has already used water marketing. In the 1990s, California conducted a water transfer in response to a seven-year drought that began in 1987. In 1991, water agencies arranged short-term water transfers within the state. The state bought surplus water from farmers' groundwater supplies and sold it to users where the drought hit the hardest. Transferring water, particularly from farms to cities, is a controversial issue. That's because whoever controls a region's water controls its future. For example, the decision to sell water to a city might make money for the seller, but it might also put local farmers out of business if they cannot maintain their crops.

Another way cities can get water is through buying land with a water source. Then, the city can transport the water on the land to the city's residence. For instance, the Los Angeles water department bought thousands of acres in the state's Central Valley just to export its water. Could buying water from an outside source be an option in Fresno?

These cases show that transferring water can raise many issues. One of the concerns is that farmers could deplete groundwater supplies to make money. That means there would not be enough water left to maintain healthy fields and grow crops. Plus, one farmer depleting groundwater supplies could impact the entire community that depended on that groundwater. There is also the risk that farmers will quit farming to become water salesmen. What would happen to our economy (and our diets) without these farmers? Some people believe that water transfers cause temperature and flow changes, which can be harmful to the surrounding environment. Others see it as part of the solution to meeting rising urban demands. They argue that water marketing decreases the need for new water projects and storage facilities. Finally, there is an ethical issue. Should water, something essential to all life, be turned into a product only for those who can afford it?

## Analysis Questions

1. Who would benefit from water marketing in the Fresno region?

2. Do you think water should be distributed equally to everyone, or should people who can afford more water be able to buy more?

3. Is access to water a basic human right? If it is a basic right, how much water is each individual entitled to receive? If it is not a basic right, what factors should determine a person's access to water? Explain your answer.

4. Answer the essential question: *How does water marketing affect your decision about the water management proposals?*

# Supporting Local Farms

***Essential Question:*** *What affect will each of the three water management proposals have on local farms?*

You are about to read a testimonial from the owner of a small family farm. As you read, think about the social and economic impacts each water management proposal might have on Leonard and his family. Then, answer the Analysis Questions.

## Supporting Local Farms

My name is Leonard James, and I have been farming this part of the Central Valley since the day I started walking. This farm is full of many memories for me. I've been working this land at my father's side ever since I could walk. We live in a time when so many people move from house to house, and even from state to state. I take pride in being able to say I have lived my whole life on the same land where my great-grandfather was born. The community history is all around us. For example, in the 1930s, my grandfather built what was then the local auction house. Although the building is now used as a community theater, it is still called Thelma's Place, after my great-grandmother.

Because our family has lived here for generations, we have very personal ties to our community. We have friendships with other local families that go back several generations. Our community means a lot to us. That's why we locals do as much charitable work as we can. Last year, for example, my wife and I were involved in organizing a fundraiser for promoting literacy among migrant farm workers. This type of community activism is fairly common among most of the farm owners we know. You are not going to find a group of people as dedicated to the land and to California as family farmers.

I'm proud of our community, and our family farm. We only have 50 acres, but thanks to the amazing climate, we can grow crops for nine or tens months of the year. That means as soon as we've harvested one crop we can usually plant another. I love knowing what a difference our family makes. People all over the country depend on us, and other families like ours, to put fresh fruits and vegetables on the table. I take great pride in what we do, and I can't wait to watch my sons and daughters carry on the family tradition.

Sometimes I worry though that we won't be able to maintain the farm long enough for that to happen. You see, our farm is small, and higher water prices put a strain on our budget. We need to be able to produce enough crops to earn a profit, and higher water prices make that difficult. Someday, it might cost more to water and maintain the farm than what we earn from selling our produce. Shortages hurt us, too. What can we do if there's not enough water to keep our crops alive? Farming is our family's way of life; it is our love. Without this land, without water for this land, I don't know what we would do.

## Analysis Questions

1. Does Mr. James mention any economic reasons to support local farms?

2. What value can you place on a community and its traditions?

3. Answer the essential question: *What affect will each of the three water management proposals have on local farms?*

# Wetlands Restoration

 **Essential Question:** *What effect will the three water management proposals have on wetlands restoration?*

## Overview

In the Soil Chapter, you learned about the three characteristics that scientists use to classify areas as wetlands. In this reading, you will be looking at how communities are trying to change back land to wetland status. Read the following article on wetland restoration and answer the Analysis Questions.

## Wetlands Restoration

Wetlands are unique places that play a number of important roles in nature. Wetlands are an essential part of the water cycle. They improve water quality by filtering surface water. Wetlands store excess rainwater, so they can reduce flooding from heavy rains. Wetlands also provide habitat to a wide variety of plants and animals. They are home to many species, including fish, amphibians, migratory birds, and a number of mammals.

When humans drain wetlands for farming or build on them for other human activities, there are consequences for both the natural environment and for humans.

The organisms that are most affected by the loss of wetlands are the ones that live in the wetlands. Some freshwater fish need wetlands to spawn. When wetlands are drained, these fish cannot reproduce, so their populations decrease. Birds also depend on wetlands. Wetland bird species feed on the fish, plants, and aquatic organisms that live in wetlands and many rely on wetland plants to hide their eggs and young. Other organisms that do not spend their entire lives in wetlands can also be affected by the loss of wetlands. Scientists estimate that more than fifty percent of the migratory birds that pass through the United States during their migration depend on wetlands for food and reproduction. Many migratory birds that travel through California in the Spring and Fall rely on California wetlands as stopover locations on their migrations. These wetlands provide them with the food and rest that they need on their long journeys. For all these organisms that depend on wetlands for their survival, the loss of wetlands means a decrease in their populations.

However, some species respond to the loss of wetlands by turning to surrounding areas to meet their survival needs. For example, some animals can learn to find food and shelter in residential neighborhoods when they lose their natural wetland habitats. Many people are not comfortable sharing their neighborhoods with these wild species. Occasionally, the new landscapes are similar enough to wetlands that plants and animals move into human developments. For instance, since the 1920s, half the wetlands in the Everglades National Park in Florida have been drained to create farmland and residential and commercial structures. In response, alligators occasionally migrate into pools and golf course lagoons in their search for a new home. This results in a clash between people and nature that can be dangerous for everyone involved. Similarly, when wetlands disappear, birds will sometimes learn to find food in trash cans of parking lots and outdoor malls.

The impact of wetland loss is not limited to other species. There are negative consequences for humans when wetlands are converted to other uses. For example, flooding can become a problem in areas where wetlands historically absorbed the precipitation associated with heavy rains. Similarly, the water quality in ground water can worsen when wetlands are not longer there to filter water as it flows into the ground.

Over the past 200 years, 54% of the wetlands that used to exist in the U.S. have been altered or destroyed. Some have been drained so the water could be used for agriculture. Others have been built over for urban development. California has suffered the worst percentage loss. The state used to be home to 3 to 5 million areas of wetlands. Now there are only 450,000 acres of wetlands in California. That is over an 85% decrease. Historically, governments encouraged people to drain wetlands because they only considered the negative impacts of wetlands, such as providing breeding grounds for mosquitoes, which can carry harmful diseases. Even when they have not focused on the negative qualities about wetlands, people have tended to value the use of wetlands for human activities more highly than their values for controlling flooding, improving water quality, and providing habitat for native species.

However, people now recognize the value of wetlands. So, since 1992, government agencies have been working to restore or create 100,000 acres of wetlands every year. However, even with this effort the U.S. still losses more wetlands than it gains every year. Restoration involves returning a damaged wetland to its former state. Creating new wetlands means converting other land into wetlands. Wetlands can be restored by removing human development and reintroducing native species. For example, if a ditch was built to drain a wetland, the ditch can be blocked so the area floods again. Then wetland plants and animals can be brought back into the habitat. New wetlands can be created by blocking streams or re-routing them to flood land that had previously been dry. When land managers restore or create wetlands, they try to mimic the natural flows of water in that location. So, in some locations, they make sure that the wetland is flooded throughout the year, and in others, they manage the flow of water to create patterns of wet and dry seasons that will enable natural ecosystems to thrive.

## Analysis Questions

1. Why are wetlands important?

2. How might retaining or restoring wetlands help Fresno's water budget?

3. What benefits do wetlands have on ecology?

4. Answer the essential question: *What effect will the three water management proposals have on wetland restoration?*

# National Dependence

**?** ***Essential Question:*** *How does the national reliance on California agriculture affect your decision on the water management proposals?*

Read the following article and answer the Analysis Questions.

## The National Dependence on California Farming

Have you ever thought about where all your fresh fruits, vegetables and nuts come from? Large portions of these produce items come from California. In fact, California farms grow over half of the U.S.'s produce. California also exports 14% of its produce. So what is it exactly that California produces? Almost all the U.S.'s almonds, artichokes, brussel sprouts, dates, figs, kiwi, olives, persimmons, pistachios, pomegranates, prunes, raisins, sweet rice, and walnuts come from California. Most of the U.S.'s tomatoes, grapes, plums, nectarines, avocados and strawberries are from California, too. If California grew less of these items, the prices of produce would increase. People would have to pay more since there would not be as much available. You can see why California farming is so important to the U.S.

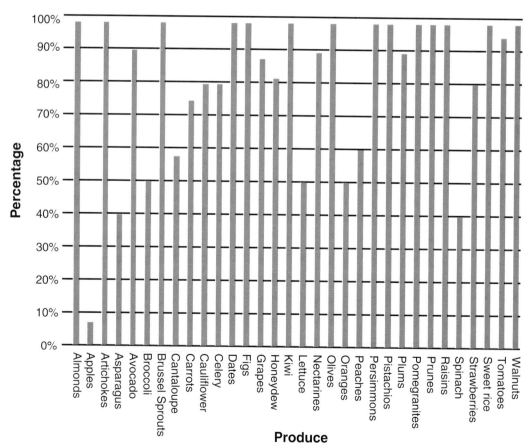

**Percentage of U.S. Produce from California**

Even though 50% of our produce comes from California, the state only has 4% of the country's farms and ranches. Nine of the ten top farming counties are in California. Fresno County is the number one farming county. In fact, Fresno grew more produce then twenty-two states. How do such a small fraction of farms grow such a large proportion of the U.S.'s produce? Part of this is that farms in other areas produce different kinds of crops. However, California's success is mostly due to its mild climate and fertile soil. These qualities allow farmers to farm multiple types of produce and have longer growing seasons.

The U.S. depends on California's farms for other reasons. In 2002, California farms made $27.5 billion. Much of that money went to the workers. However, some also went to the government as taxes. In California, one out of ten people have a job related to farming. Californian farming creates 184,000 export jobs. It also creates jobs for truckers, packagers, and vendors. California farming creates more than $100 billion of income per year.

## Analysis Questions

1. What fraction of the vegetables in your local grocery store comes from California?

2. Are you willing to give up or pay more for produce if California crop production declines?

3. Answer the essential question: *How does the national reliance on California agriculture affect your decision on the water management proposals?*

# Lesson 4

# Decision and Presentations

***Driving Question:*** *What is the best solution to Fresno's water problem?*

## Overview

In this lesson, you will use the Environmental Decision Making process to balance the consequences and stakeholders for each option. You have all the information you need. You have statistics about water availability and an understanding of political concerns. Use that information to choose a solution that meets your constraints and criteria. Remember, there is no one right answer to this problem – there are only different choices. Make sure you support your decision with evidence. Make a convincing case that your decision was a good one.

## Important Content

• Many different issues are involved in deciding how to address a region's water problems.

• Farmers, environmentalists, and ordinary citizens all have a stake in the outcome.

# Narrowing Options

 **Essential Question:** *How do these three choices fit the constraints and considerations you feel are most important?*

## Overview

In this activity, you will compare the proposals you researched in Lesson 2: *Proposal Analysis*. As a group, you will need to come to a consensus about which option is the best one. As you discuss the different options, remember to use evidence to support what you are saying. Use the readings from earlier in the chapter to better understand the consequences of each proposal. Use your group list of constraints and considerations to guide your choices and eliminate unsuitable options.

## Procedure

With your group, draw Cascading Consequence Charts for all three proposals. Use the charts to determine whether each choice meets your constraints and considerations.

## Analysis Questions

1. For each of the three proposals, your group should turn in a Cascading Consequence Chart. The chart should cover consequences to the environment and the community. The charts should include effects like:

   a. How will farmers need to change their practices if this proposal is passed? Will they still be able to grow the same crops?

   b. Will people in the cities be affected by the proposal? If so, how?

   c. How will the proposal affect the environment?

2. Answer the essential question: *How do these three choices fit the constraints and considerations you feel are most important?*

# Investigate Impacts

**Essential Questions:** *Which stakeholders will be most affected by your decision? Do those stakeholders have the power to make the decision?*

## Overview

Now that you have consequence charts for the three proposals, it is time to look at each one more closely. In this activity, you will construct stakeholder charts. Remember that stakeholders are people, organizations, the environment, etc, that will be affected by your decision. The chart you make in this activity will help you organize the consequences in a different way. It will give you a picture of all the ways that each stakeholder will be affected. It is important to know whether the effect is your intended goal or a side effect. An option with many unintended side effects might not be the best one to choose. Another important aspect of side effects, and negative effects in general, is consent. Did the stakeholder consent to be a part of this process or decision? Think about the responsibilities decision makers have for the consequences of their actions.

## Procedure

1. Based on your consequence charts and research, create a list of stakeholders.

2. As a group, complete the stakeholders chart for each of the three options.

## Analysis Questions

1. How did you narrow your list of stakeholders?

2. How are the stakeholders related to your list of constraints and criteria?

3. Do you believe that decision makers are responsible for the unintended effects of the decisions they make? Why or why not?

4. Answer the essential questions: *Which stakeholders will be most affected by your decision? Do those stakeholders have the power to make the decision?*

## Stakeholders for Option #1

| Who are the **stakeholders** that will be affected by this action? | In what way(s) will they be affected? | + or − | Is this effect the intended goal of the action or is it a side effect? | Has the stakeholder placed himself/herself in this position voluntarily and with appropriate understanding of the risks involved? | How inportant to YOU are the interests of this stakeholder?  1=very important 2=somewhat important 3=unimportant | If the effect is negative, do YOU feel it is directly offset by greater good elsewhere? |
|---|---|---|---|---|---|---|
| | | | | | | |
| | | | | | | |
| | | | | | | |
| | | | | | | |
| | | | | | | |
| | | | | | | |
| | | | | | | |
| | | | | | | |
| | | | | | | |

## Stakeholders for Option #2

| Who are the stakeholders that will be affected by this action? | In what way(s) will they be affected? | + or − | Is this effect the intended goal of the action or is it a side effect? | Has the stakeholder placed himself/herself in this position voluntarily and with appropriate understanding of the risks involved? | How important to YOU are the interests of this stakeholder? 1=very important 2=somewhat important 3=unimportant | If the effect is negative, do YOU feel it is directly offset by greater good elsewhere? |
|---|---|---|---|---|---|---|
| | | | | | | |
| | | | | | | |
| | | | | | | |
| | | | | | | |
| | | | | | | |
| | | | | | | |
| | | | | | | |
| | | | | | | |

## Stakeholders for Option #3

| Who are the **stakeholders** that will be affected by this action? | In what way(s) will they be affected? | + or − | Is this effect the intended goal of the action or is it a side effect? | Has the stakeholder placed himself/ herself in this position voluntarily and with appropriate understanding of the risks involved? | How important to YOU are the interests of this stakeholder?  1 = very important  2 = somewhat important  3 = unimportant | If the effect is negative, do YOU feel it is directly offset by greater good elsewhere? |
|---|---|---|---|---|---|---|
| | | | | | | |
| | | | | | | |
| | | | | | | |
| | | | | | | |
| | | | | | | |
| | | | | | | |
| | | | | | | |
| | | | | | | |
| | | | | | | |

# Make a Decision

**Essential Question:** *What is the best decision? Consider all stakeholders, consequences, constraints, and considerations.*

## Analysis Questions

1. Answer the essential question: *What is the best decision? Consider all stakeholders, consequences, constraints, and considerations.*

   • Make sure to cover each constraint and consideration you listed.

   • Make sure to explain how any negative effects are outweighed by the positives.

# Present your decision

***Essential Question:*** *What were the major obstacles to this decision?*

## Overview

An important part of environmental decision-making is supporting your claims with evidence. As you prepare your report and presentation, remember that you are trying to convince people that your decision is a good one. Use evidence from the rest of Unit 3 to support your opinions and your decision. Use logic to describe why you made your decision. Give the reasons why you rejected some options. Include your values and opinions in your decision, but make sure to support what you are saying with facts and evidence.

## Procedure

1. Compile a report that includes:
   - a list of your group constraints and considerations
   - a complete description of the three proposals
   - consequence charts, and stakeholder charts for all three proposals
   - a decision statement that describes how you met each constraint and consideration

2. Answer the Analysis Questions below.

3. Give a 5-minute presentation that includes:
   - a summary of why you chose the proposal you did
   - your predictions of the consequences of that proposal

## Analysis Questions

1. Are you satisfied with your decision? Why or why not?

2. Is there anything you would change if you had the chance to make the decision again?

3. Answer the essential question: *What were the major obstacles to this decision?*

# Glossary

**Agricultural pumpage** – water pumped from the aquifer for use in agriculture

**Alevin** – salmon that have just hatched from eggs, retaining a yolk sac which they slowly absorb

**Aquifer** – an underground area where water fills the pore spaces between soil and rock

**Arch dam** – concrete dam built in a steep canyon, using the strength of an arch shape to hold water back

**Available water capacity** – the amount of water held by the soil that is available to plants; the difference between the wilting point and the field capacity

**Bedrock** – solid rock underlying soil

**Biomass** – plant material, vegetation, or agricultural waste used as a fuel or energy source

**Brassica** – genus of the mustard family including cabbage and turnips

**Bushel** – a unit of volume or used in dry measure equal to 2,150.42 cubic inches, or 35.24 liters

**Buttress dam** – tall concrete dams that use a series of supports, or buttresses, to support the pressure from the water

**Clay** – material composed mainly of fine particles and minerals

**Compost** – a mixture that consists primarily of decayed organic matter that is used for fertilizing and conditioning land

**Condensation** – the conversion of water vapor to a liquid

**Cone of depression** – a dip or depression in the water table caused by suction from a well

**Confined aquifer** – an aquifer that is bound by a confining layer. Often this refers to aquifers that are under a confining layer.

**Confining layer** – a layer of impermeable rock or clay that will not allow water to pass through quickly or at all

**Conservation** – practices associated with protecting natural and undeveloped areas

**Contour lines** – lines on a topographic map that indicate elevation at fixed intervals

**Decommission** – to withdraw from active service. For dams, this often means taking down the dam to restore natural waterways.

**Discharge** – stream flow in a river

**Drawdown** – a reduction in the amount of water in an aquifer as a result of more being taken out of the aquifer than is recharged or added

**Embankment dam** – (a.k.a. earth dam) dam made of earth and rock that holds water back with its own bulk

**Eradication** – to get rid of, remove

**Evaporation** – the conversion of liquid water into a gas

**Evapotranspiration** – a loss of water from the soil both by evaporation and by transpiration from plants

**Evidence** – something that furnishes proof

**Fast plant** – a variety of leafy brassica plant that grows very rapidly

**Fertilizer** – a substance farmers place on the land to add nutrients to the soil

**Field capacity** – the maximum amount of water that a soil can hold

**Fish ladder** – a structure built beside a dam that has concrete steps with water running down it. These steps allow salmon passage to swim upstream to spawning grounds.

**Fry** – young salmon that have absorbed their yolk sac and emerged from the gravel beds

**Furrow** – a trough dug in the ground between rows of crops for delivery of irrigation water

**Glacier** – large body of ice

**Global Positioning System** – (GPS) a device that uses triangulation of signals from a constellation of satellites to identify the location on the Earth's surface

**Gravity dam** – dam made of concrete that holds water back with its own bulk

**Groundwater flow** – movement of water underground through aquifers

**Horizon** – the distinct layers of soil and underlying material in vertical sections of land

**Humus** – the brown or black part of the organic matter. Humus results from partial decomposition of plant or animal matter. Humus is one part of soil organic matter, which has three components – 1) living biomass, 2) dead roots and other recognizable tissue, and 3) humus.

**Hydrograph** – a graph that shows seasonal and yearly changes in the flow or discharge of a waterway

**Hydroponic** – growing plants in another medium other than soil

**Impermeable** – an impermeable substance does not let water pass through it

**Infiltration** – the movement of water from the surface of the ground into the soil

**Inorganic** – made from non-living things

**Irrigation** – the application of water to a field to provide enough water for growing plants

**Juvenile** – young organism

**Loam** – a soil consisting of a mixture of clay, silt and sand

**Macro-nutrients** – chemical elements which are needed in relatively large quantities for the growth of plants

**Mortality rate** – ratio of deaths in an area to the populations of that area

**Municipal pumpage** – water pumped from the aquifer for use in urban and residential areas

**Nitrates** – a chemical compound containing nitrogen and oxygen

**Nitrogen fixation** – the process where soil microorganisms make nitrogen in the atmosphere available for plant use

**Non-point source pollution** – pollution that comes from a more generalized area, like runoff from farms, or water that picks up pollution from city streets

**Opinion** – a view, judgment, or appraisal formed in the mind about a particular matter

**Organic** – derived from living organisms

**Organic farming** – a method of farming that does not use artificial chemical fertilizers or pesticides

**Outlet works** – a series of openings located in a dam through which water is released from the reservoir

**Oven dry** – soil that has no water in its pore spaces or held by soil particles

**Peat moss** – sphagnum moss that grows only in wet, acidic areas that compacts and partially decomposes to form peat

**Ped** – a natural soil mass or cluster

**Percolation** – trickling of a liquid substance through a permeable substance

**Permanent wilting point** – when the plant cannot pull water from the plant-rooting zone and the plant wilts

**Permeability** – a measurement of the pores or openings that permit liquids or gases to pass through

**Permeable** – a permeable substance will let water pass through it

**Pinniped** – a suborder of carnivorous aquatic mammals that includes the seals, walruses, and similar animals having finlike flippers as organs of locomotion

**Point source pollution** – pollution that comes from a specific location, for example, an underground gasoline tank

**Porosity** – the ratio of the volume of the pores in a material, such as soil, to the volume of its mass

**Precipitation** – rain or snowfall

**Precision farming** – the management of an agricultural crop at a spatial scale smaller than the individual field. This usually involves the use of GPS and GIS software to monitor fertilizer and water application and crop yield on specific areas of fields.

**Predator** – an organism that lives by preying on (eating) other organisms

**Recharge basin** – a shallow pool of water that is allowed to percolate slowly down into the aquifer

**Recharge zone** – an area on the surface above, or adjacent to, an aquifer that water seeps through to reach the aquifer. Often the recharge zone is directly above an aquifer, but it can also be to the sides

**Redd** – a nest made by a female salmon where she lays her eggs

**Reservoir** – an artificial lake that forms behind a dam

**Saltwater intrusion** – movement of saltwater from the ocean into an overdrawn freshwater aquifer

**Sand** – a loose granular material that results from the erosion or breakdown of rocks; consists of particles smaller than gravel but coarser than silt

**Saturation** – the point at which all available spaces are filled to capacity. For example, when all the pores in soil have been filled with water the soil is saturated, and any additional water will run off.

**Sediment** – solid fragments of inorganic or organic material that comes from the weathering of rock or fragmentation of vegetation and animals. These fragments are then carried and deposited by rivers, oceans, or wind.

**Sieve** – a series of mesh screens through which finer particles of a mixture are passed in order to separate them from coarser ones

**Silt** – loose sedimentary material with particles smaller than sand but coarser than clay

**Sinkhole** – a small, quickly sinking depression in the ground, often a result of too much water being removed from an aquifer

**Smolts** – young salmon that have migrated down river and have already become tolerant to the salt in seawater

**Spillway** – the dam's overflow channel. It is used in emergencies, such as floods, to release the water from the reservoir before the pressure on the dam gets too high

**Sport fish** – fish that are popular to catch

**Sublimation** – the conversion of ice to water vapor

**Subsidence** – a lowering in elevation of the surface of the ground due to rock or soil collapsing underneath. This often occurs when too much water is removed from an aquifer.

**Texture triangle** – a tool used by soil scientists to determine soil type based on percentage of sand, silt, and clay in the soil

**Topographic map** – a two-dimensional map that uses contour lines to indicate elevation of a particular area

**Transpiration** – passage of water vapor from a living body through a membrane or pores. This can happen in plants or animals.

**Unconfined aquifer** – an aquifer that is not bound by a confining layer

**Urban intentional recharge** – water that is returned to the aquifer through drainage basins. Urban intentional recharge is often located in urban areas.

**Urban sprawl** – the rapid growth and development of an urban area. Urban sprawl often encroaches on land formerly used for agriculture or natural areas.

**Water meter** – a device attached to a home or business that measures the amount of water used. This is normally used to determine the customer's water bill.

**Water table** – the depth to which a well must be drilled in order to reach an aquifer.

**Watershed** – area of land through which water flows on its way to a water body (lake, river or ocean)

**Yield** – an amount produced

# Index